Reality Check
For
Leaders

A workable approach to
maximizing your results
as a leader in the
Hospitality Industry.

Frank J. Schilagi, Ph.D.

First edition copyright © 2007 Frank J. Schilagi, Ph.D.

ISBN 978-0-9794381-6-5
Library of Congress Control Number 2007903123
Published by Directions Incorporated, North Carolina
Edited by: Scott C. Schilagi
Design and layout by: Kyleene W. Blalock

Printed in the United States of America by: JOSTENS INCORPORATED
2505 Empire Drive, Winston Salem, NC. 27103

CONTENTS

	Prologue	4
Chapter 1	The Cast of Characters	6
Chapter 2	A Leader Listens and Learns	19
Chapter 3	Perception Is the Only Reality	33
Chapter 4	Different Payoffs for Different People	48
Chapter 5	This Will Be on the Test	61
Chapter 6	Unused Knowledge Has No Value	74
Chapter 7	Beginner's Luck or the Real Thing?	93
Chapter 8	Face Time with the Vice President	106
Chapter 9	Back to the Drawing Board	119
Chapter 10	Motivating Up and Down	132
Chapter 11	This Is Reality Check	147
Chapter 12	How Do You Get to...? Practice, Practice, Practice	162
Chapter 13	But Will RCL Work at My Hotel?	175
Chapter 14	You Didn't Just Miss the Boat... You Missed the Dock	192
Chapter 15	Maybe More Than I Want to Know about Me	210
Chapter 16	An Organization's Reward System	229
Chapter 17	Reality Check in Action	245
Chapter 18	265 Days Later	259
Chapter 19	The Home Stretch	275
	Epilogue	285
	Chapter Attributions	288
	References and Acknowledgements	290

PROLOGUE

Walking in from the cold and rainy parking lot, I wonder about my rule that we all have to park in the secondary lots and leave the close spots for our guests. I say good morning to our night auditor and walk to the kitchen to get a cup of coffee.

As I carry my coffee to my office, I hear an explosion coming from the Sales Department. I run down the hall and come face to face with a woman walking toward me. I notice two things: There is a car in the hallway of my hotel, and the woman is holding her panties and wearing nothing. Maybe I should have been a detective. I put my jacket around her and ask, "Are you hurt?"

"No."

"Where are your clothes?"

"In the car."

The car, a small Ford sedan, is actually in the hallway fronting the Sales Department. One wheel, raised in the air, is slowly turning. Stepping over plasterboard, strips of aluminum and glass, I shut the engine off and look through the huge hole in the wall. I notice a pair of men's slacks, a shoe, shorts, and a jacket, but no man.

I find her jeans and tank top. After she puts them on, they look as if they have been spray-painted onto her body.

"What's your name and what happened?" I ask.

Victoria tells me she came to the bar last night with some friends to celebrate the return of her driver's license after a one-year suspension. As the night progressed, a man staying in the hotel asked her to dance. Before long, they were sitting and talking. By the time Victoria and her new friend closed the bar, they decided they were in love. Unfortunately, he had a roommate, so they went to her car, which was parked in front of the Sales Office, and started the engine to keep warm.

Well, one thing led to another, and, in a moment of passion, one of them pressed down on the accelerator and the other knocked the gearshift out of park and into drive. The result: a short but very fast ride through the windows of the Sales Department. The car and its almost naked passengers knocked over a reception desk, three filing cabinets, and some chairs. The car continued and knocked down two non-load-bearing walls and pulled a major section of the ceiling down. Plowing through the sitting area, it finally stopped halfway into the hall. Victoria says her friend, wasting no time, got out of the car and took the elevator to his room.

She either is in a daze or very relaxed while telling me the story, although when the police arrive, she grabs my arm.

The officers take down her story and try to find out the name of the man. Victoria will not say and the police tell me that because she was not trying to drive, it is up to me to press charges. I figure that since no one was hurt and she and her insurance company will pay for the damages, enough is enough. She thanks us all and goes to the room I arranged for her so she can rest and sober up. I don't know when she will leave or if ever again she will see the only man she really cares about.

As I stand there watching the crew cover the windows and surveying the damage, Tom, one of our hotel security guards, walks up and says, "We stopped a woman from stealing table lamps from her room last night, and now she is threatening to sue the hotel."

I look at my watch; it is 6:10 a.m.

So you want to run a hotel. WELCOME!

CHAPTER ONE

THE CAST OF CHARACTERS

I would write of the universal, not the provincial, in human nature....I would write of characters, not of characteristics.

Ellen Glasgow

My name is John J. Battaglia. I am forty-three years old, stand about six feet tall, and weigh 190 pounds when I push myself at the club and over 200 if I don't. I was born and raised in Buffalo, New York, when Buffalo was a thriving industrial city. All four of my grandparents came from Italy in the early 1900s. They loved the United States and would not allow anyone to speak Italian in their homes. Consequently, I know very little Italian—just the street words I learned on the West Side. I'm successful in what I do and have made some good investments over the years. I drive expensive cars and wear tailored clothes.

The people who don't understand that you can succeed by working hard and smart sometimes say that my money comes from a family connection. What they are thinking is the Mafia. I admit I sometimes encourage that way of thinking just for the fun of watching the reactions. People who know me think I have a good sense of humor; the people who don't sometimes think I am a smart aleck. Whatever.

I went to college at a small school about 125 miles from the "city." Everyone who lives in New York State calls New York City, "the city," as if it is the only one in the world. One of the reasons for picking Delhi College was that it was close to the city. Another was the hotel program.

I had worked as a bellman and a desk clerk in a large downtown hotel in Buffalo as a teenager. I enjoyed the environment and the excitement that is inherent in the hotel business. Delhi had a very good reputation in the industry, and I wanted to learn more. I was not on the Dean's List while in school but received a good, solid education. In fact, I believe that my experience at Delhi has carried me a long way in the business. As it turns out, a degree from Delhi means a lot to people in the hotel/restaurant business.

I'm the general manager of the Diamond Creek Inn, which is part of the Blackwood Hotels and Resorts franchise. The "D," as we call the hotel, has 300 guestrooms, 155 suites, 2 restaurants, a 500-seat lounge, and 15,000 square feet of meeting space. It is five years old. I am also responsible for overseeing the operation of a nearby 120-room Hampton Inn with two small meeting rooms. The Hampton was opened ten years ago. Both are located in Charlotte, North Carolina, and both are coming out of a serious hotel recession that started about six months ago. The downturn was caused by an incredible amount of overbuilding and a Convention and Visitors

Bureau (CVB) that was, for all intents and purposes, useless for a variety of reasons.

The number of rooms available in Charlotte had almost doubled in three years—from seventeen thousand to thirty-one thousand—while the bookings for big citywide conventions continued to drop.

During every monthly meeting of the Hospitality Tourism Alliance (HTA), hotel general managers (GMs) and others in the city tried to put pressure on the CVB to get more convention business. Nothing seemed to work.

About a year ago, with the strong support of the president of the HTA, the CVB had a change in organizational structure and the future looked much brighter. We were all encouraged by what seemed to be progress within the organization. However, the new business being generated was for the future and could not help current revenue problems. I know it will take another year to show progress, so my job is to hold both places together until occupancy levels improve.

A real estate investment trust (REIT) owns the D. As long as Matrix, the management company, sends the interest and principal check for $82,000 every month, the trust leaves us alone.

The Hampton is owned by Waldo Cluster, a two-bit millionaire who is the general partner and shows up on random occasions to make off-the-wall, stream-of-consciousness decisions. After almost running the Hampton into the ground, Cluster was forced by the limited partners to hire a management company. He resents Matrix and its people because we turned the property around.

Because Cluster is the general partner, Matrix must listen to what he says. However, they have an unwritten policy of ignoring him as much as possible. I've attended some meetings with him and it is obvious that this guy couldn't manage his own life, let alone a real company. That major flaw is compounded by the fact that the business community perceives him as a small-time, not-too-bright crook. His pronouncements about what is "absolutely the right thing to do" are always good for a laugh. In other words, he is a pain and makes everyone's job tougher than it has to be and less fun than it could be. Much of what I do for the Hampton involves helping people overcome his stupid, insensitive behavior.

Word has it that Cluster is worth about $9 million. Part two is that his father left him about $30 million.

He is not necessarily an exception. There are many hotel owners who have more money than brains. Cluster is a perfect example of that. In fact, if he had nothing but a quarter, he would still have more money than brains.

YOU SHOULD KNOW

Good leaders have a low tolerance for people who get in the way of results.

4:45 A.M. I arrive at the D. It is still dark and the hotel is just starting to come alive. I always find this time of morning to be restful on the surface while projecting a sense of excitement about what the day will bring.

That, I think, is one of the rewards of working in this business. People who are not in the hotel business might not understand, but I do; that feeling is one reason I show up so early.

By the way, I am not a seven-day-a-week GM. When I need to get away, I do. Sometimes the pressure is so great that I have to take a break. My health club is a great place to work off stress. In addition, just driving on country roads through small, quiet towns is relaxing. I do whatever it takes to get some balance in my life.

4:52 A.M. Here I am, in before the chickens are up, headed to the back office. I say hello to Janet, the night auditor. You cannot find a more productive and loyal employee. She is in her seventies and shows no signs of slowing. In fact, Matrix uses her to train most of its night auditors.

"Hi, Janet, how's it going?"

"Horrible. I can't believe those people in O'Brian's can't balance their drawers. They were off $230. And it took me an hour to find their mistake."

"Okay, calm down. What caused the problem?"

"It's those airheads you hire for servers. They're so busy counting their tips that they don't have time to check their tickets. And another thing, I think someone is stealing from us. There were five tickets missing from the number sequence tonight and that's the second time this month."

"I'll check into the missing tickets with Danny [the lounge manager] and maybe we can have another class on how to use our tickets."

"It won't do any good. You keep hiring these bimbos and most can't tell the time of day," Janet replies angrily.

"Maybe, Janet," I laugh, "but they sure bring in the business at night. And we have a big place to fill every night."

"Well, it's never going to take. They don't stay long enough to learn anything if they could."

She is right. The turnover is high. When you hire attractive women and men to be servers, you face the risk that they will get other offers that seem better at the time and move on. But after trying another company and eventually coming back to us, they turn out to be better employees. I tell Janet that I'll work on the problem and we'll talk later.

5:03 A.M. As I leave Janet's office, Vance walks up.

"Good morning," he says. "We have a problem in the boiler room. We may not have hot water for these people today."

"These 'people', as you put it, are the reason we have jobs."

10

"I know, I know, and I got it fixed around four this morning. Maybe it will have time to heat enough water."

"We have about 280 in the house, and most will be up between 6:30 and 7:30," I tell him.

"Then we should be all right. How come we don't have any business?"

"Well, actually, we are up above last year but just not enough yet."

"The staff is worried about keeping their jobs."

What he really means is, "I am worried about keeping my job."

"They have no reason to worry, and thanks for fixing that boiler. What time did you get here?"

"I got a call from Janet around three this morning."

"Go home and get some rest. We can cover for you."

"Yeah, okay."

We both know that he won't leave. He gets part of his kicks from amazing people with his dedication and hard work. I thank Vance again and head for my office.

5:11 A.M. I make a pot of coffee in the little alcove next to my office and turn on my computer. As I enter my office, I spot the book on the end of my desk—the book that college professor gave me to read.

I met him last night at the GM's reception. I was talking to a group of Duke Energy managers who were going to attend his seminar today.

"What is his topic?" I asked them.

"Something about a belief system." One of them said.

I got a laugh when I replied, "Oh, I already have a religion."

Then Tracy, the director of sales and marketing, walked up with a gentleman whom she introduced to the Duke people as the speaker for the seminar, Dr. Mark Spencer. I recognized immediately that he did not want to be at this party. He was not nervous; he was bored.

I walked over to him. "Hello, I'm John Battaglia, the general manager of the Diamond. Welcome. I bet you'd rather be doing anything but this."

IIe laughed. "You hit it right on the money. I come to these things because I'm expected to. I would rather be out on the interstate counting cars."

"What are you going to be teaching tomorrow?"

"Reality Check for Leaders."

I looked away. "Oh," slipped out.

Spencer smiled. "You're thinking it's another dog and pony show."

"No, I'm sure it's special. Duke Energy wouldn't waste the time of twenty-five of its top people if you weren't good. I'm sure what you have to say will help these Duke people. I wish I had something to help me motivate my people to get better results and meet the goals of our organization."

"Organizations don't have goals, John."

"What?" Great, another college professor.

"That's right. It's the people in organizations that have goals."

"Isn't that just using different definitions of the same thing?"

"If you believe that your organization has goals, you must be disappointed a lot."

"Well, I'm sure your approach works fine for the big corporate types, but I deal with a different kind of organization with really different people problems," I said with more defensiveness in my voice than I intended.

Just then Harrison Motley, the conference coordinator for the Duke Energy seminar, walked up. "John, I see you've met Dr. Spencer."

"I sure have and we were having a discussion about whether his theory would work in the hotel industry." What I thought was that this Spencer guy is a typical Ph.D.

Harrison said, "I'll let you guys talk. We get to hear Dr. Spencer tomorrow."

"I wish I could," I said, "but we both have to make the rounds, you know, meet and greet."

Spencer smiled at my smart-aleck comment. "Harrison, I'm not going to stay too much longer. There are a few things I thought about on the plane that I want to add to tomorrow's session."

Smooth. This guy knew how to get out of situations he didn't like. I wondered how many times he had used that line.

As I walked away, I said, "Good to meet you Dr. Spencer. I hope tomorrow goes great for you."

"Why not sit in? Harrison likes you and I'm sure he wouldn't mind."

"Thank you very much, but I'm not sure I can get away for an entire day on such short notice. But more important, I don't want to impose on my clients."

KNOWING YOU

Do you jump at the opportunity to learn something new or do you resist because you think all change is destructive?

"Okay, let's do this," Spencer said. "I will get approval from Harrison if you decide you want to come. And I want you to have a copy of my book to look over tonight."

"Great. I really appreciate your time and interest."

"If you send someone to my room in a few minutes, I'll send back a copy of my book."

"Okay, I'll get that done and, again, thanks for your time."

I paged Tony and told him to follow Dr. Spencer to his room, get the book, and put it in my office.

As the reception wound down, I said my goodbyes and headed to my office where I found Dr. Spencer's book sitting on my desk. No textbook tonight. I wanted to go home, eat, finish the John Updike book, *Roger's Version*, and watch the car auction on Speedvision. No deep thinking. Enough work.

Now here it is Thursday and I haven't read the book or thought any more about going to the seminar. Maybe I'll stay in my office until the seminar begins and just miss Dr. Spencer all day. No, that will be too much trouble. I will just tell him I'm too busy, thank him for the book, and move on.

The dust cover of the book reads *Reality Check for Leaders* in big letters. I read about the author, Dr. Mark Spencer, and I'm impressed. He's not just a college professor working in those places I call the "temples of knowledge." He has his own successful business and became a millionaire at an early age. He evidently has led banks and country clubs and was even a dean at Wake Forest University.

From our brief meeting last night, I feel he is a real person and not some dog-and-pony phony. I wonder what his book has to say. Maybe I will go with my instincts and read the book.

YOU SHOULD KNOW

Knowledge and experience equal good instincts.

Since it is still early, I decide to read some parts of the book to get an insight into his ideas about motivating people for improved results. I get a cup of coffee and open the book. I am immediately drawn to the paragraphs describing Spencer's thoughts on the latest theory to "solve all your management problems."

He writes that every year consultants, professors, and assorted human resource development professionals teach the latest theories of management and leadership. I know that those theories change almost every year. The reason for the change: *They do not work.* Why don't they work? Spencer says that almost all of these theories ignore the basic elements in motivation; and motivation, positive or negative, equals good or bad goal-oriented behavior and results.

He is right and I want to know what the answer is, given the constant pressure to improve results. I do know that while all seminars promise to teach a way of getting things done with people, and most provide a method that might work, the result is always the same: Two weeks after I return from such a seminar, the same old people problems are still here.

What may seem like answers to our people problems in a seminar become nothing more than short-term fixes that do not last. I end up feeling as if I have wasted my time. Others I know feel the same way.

Boy, does my mind wander. What does Spencer have to say about solving people problems? I read on.

He writes that there are three elements to successful long-term motivation. When people do not behave the way they are expected to, then a leader or manager (or husband, wife, anyone) should look to these three elements that influence the difference between expected behavior and real behavior.

While I have been convinced for a long time that people only pursue personal payoffs (PPPP), Dr. Spencer adds the points of clarification necessary to bring the idea full circle. He is convinced that to motivate people it is necessary to understand important elements that determine how they behave in their interactions with others and the situations they encounter in everyday life.

As I continue to read, I learn that Spencer thinks in terms of what he calls Performance Elements:

1. People pursue only personal payoffs.
2. Rewarded behavior is repeated.

3.   Perceived skills and individual interests drive results.

While that makes a great deal of sense, I wonder how difficult it would be to apply his ideas to running a hotel.

7:15 A.M. Wow. I've been reading for over an hour and want to know more. No time now. I'm late for our breakfast guests. As I walk past the front desk to the atrium, I notice Dr. Spencer checking out. I stop at the desk.

"I hope you had a good stay, Dr. Spencer."

"It was fine," he replies. "I'm about to have breakfast. Want to join me?"

"Sure. Let me say hi to a couple of people and I will."

I walk around to the banquet area, talk to my manager about today's events, and head back to the atrium. I say good morning to a number of regulars and new people and see Dr. Spencer sitting at a two top.

"Good morning again," I say to him.

"Come sit," he tells me, pointing to the chair across from him. "Would you like to order?"

"No, I usually eat around nine or so after everything has calmed down."

"Did you know that the sooner you eat in the morning, the sooner your metabolism gets started and the more calories you burn?"

"No, but that makes sense. I'll try to remember that."

Spencer smiles. "That reminds me of what I frequently hear about my Reality Check for Leaders: 'That makes sense. I wonder why I didn't know that?'"

"Speaking of your theory, I wonder if you think it would work in a hospitality environment as well as you say it works in other organizations."

He laughs. "You get right to the point. The answer is that it does work in the manufacturing and banking industry, and I am confident that it will work in your business. We should prove it."

"How?"

"How do you think we could test my ideas in your environment?"

It is my turn to smile. "Now, Dr Spencer, you and I both know you have the answer. Why waste time waiting for me to come up with the right solution?"

He chuckles again. "You're right. I know how we might find out. Why not let me follow you around for a day or two and show you how to apply my theory when appropriate?"

"I don't think my management company would approve the expense."

"There will be no expense except for my room and meals. I have some time before I have to be at Road Atlanta for my racing class. If you have the time this week, we could do it after my seminar."

I think for a moment. How could this not be good? I have an expert, one who gets thousands of dollars a day, willing to follow me around. I might learn a more effective way of getting things done and, if not, I get a great story for the next HTA meeting.

"You got a deal," I said. "Let me know when you want to start."

"What time will you get to work in the morning?"

"Sometime before 7:00 a.m. But we could meet at eight or nine if you prefer."

"Call me anytime after 6:30 and I'll come down."

"You're on. See you tomorrow." With that, I get up and pick up his breakfast check. "We might as well start now. Have a good seminar."

I head back to my office. Thank goodness that my people know I'm constantly trying new management ideas on them. They should take this in stride. Whatever happens, I am sure, will be interesting and probably fun.

KNOWING YOU

Do you believe that being a leader can be interesting and fun or that it is just a matter of enforcing a series of rules and regulations? Is how you just answered the preceding question what you really believe?

CHAPTER TWO

A LEADER LISTENS AND LEARNS

Every act of conscious learning requires the willingness to suffer an injury to one's self-esteem.

Thomas Szasz

6:00 A.M. The weather report said it would be cold, and it is. The weekly forecast indicates a chance of snow. That could be good or bad for business, but in any case, it is always fun. I start my car and head to work. As the heater begins warming the car, I think about how I have come to this point in my life. I know I am a good general manager and wonder what decisions I have made to get here and why I am considered very good, if not excellent, at my job.

The position of general manager is fun most of the time and seems easy. However, for some it is difficult, if not impossible. There is never a time when I do not realize

I could be a better general manager. Maybe spending time with this college professor will help.

Hotel owners complain most about how hard it is to find good people. I wonder if that is really the problem. I have seen many good people hired, only to witness how often things turn sour for them. In any case, it is generally believed that finding a good GM is the most difficult part of owning a hotel. Management company executives continue to offer me positions all over the country.

The industry turnover is beyond reason, over 147% last year. Yet people are attracted to all aspects of running a hotel. Over the years, I have met hundreds of department heads in all parts of a hotel. Some are exceptional, some could be good with the right direction, many are average, and some are marginal at best. What is the difference between the best and the worst? What contributes to this bell-shaped curve of success? I know it's not magic, but what is it that determines outstanding performance?

YOU SHOULD KNOW

Your willingness to take risks and handle more than one project at a time, coupled with your need for variety, is an important factor in your leadership potential in the hotel business.

I have always known there are two factors vital to success in any field. One is the skill necessary to perform the function and the other is the level of interest in performing it. If either is lacking, the odds of being in the top 20% in one's chosen field are slim. A reasonably intelligent person could learn the basics in most areas of a hotel, but it takes someone with an abiding interest to go beyond the average.

6:30 A.M. Turning into the hotel parking lot, I wonder what the day will bring. Is the professor going to help or hinder the work that has to be done today? It's one thing to sit back in an office and develop theory after theory about how to do something, and another to have to actually solve a problem at the moment it arises. If nothing else, this guy should make the day interesting, if not rewarding.

A quick drive around the hotel reveals some landscaping issues that need attention. I know it is early and that the maintenance people will get the problems fixed when they arrive for the first shift in a couple of hours. I stop and pick up some paper cups and a discarded Coke can. Not too messy for the morning after a busy Thursday night.

I unlock my office door and turn on the computer. Walking to the kitchen, I say hello to the morning crew and stop to talk to a sous chef whose son has applied to UNC-Charlotte. I know the young man and wrote a letter of recommendation for him. Eddie, the young man's father, tells me that there is no news.

Eddie loves cooking and is a great example of someone who loves his job. I agree that the prospect of putting together a 300 plate sit-down dinner is exciting and challenging. However, the working conditions in most kitchens would be considered difficult at best by most observers; yet people like Eddie seek out food and beverage positions all the time. Amazing.

Tuesday through Thursday, hotel guests come charging down for breakfast between 6:45 and 8:30 a.m. However, with air travel costs rising, Mondays have also become busier as business people want to save money by spending the night on Sunday. That seems too big of a cost—people have to miss Sundays with their families and loved ones. No wonder more travelers are tense. Not many seem to relax and read the paper anymore. The pace of life in the hotel has increased and not, I think, for the better. There seems to be more anxiety in the atmosphere. Guests seem to be losing out to stress and are less willing to accept simple human error. I wonder if this is symptomatic of our post 9/11 culture or something more. I also wonder how much this change in our society is affecting me and the way I manage my people.

7:10 A.M. Back in my office, I review my to-do list for Friday and answer some emails. Funny how, on some days, it seems that nothing gets done. Moreover, as good as I am at prioritizing tasks, there are days when I accomplish very little of what I had planned to do.

I also know that a certain amount of change is part of the excitement of working in hospitality. There is day-to-day pressure created by managing a business that is open 24 hours a day, 365 days a year. And today I'll have Dr. Spencer with me. Someone following me around all day will be a first for me.

Today I have a payables meeting at 9 a.m., a few vendors to call or email, and after that, room inspections with the executive housekeeper. Today's schedule also includes a visit with the General Manager of the Hampton Inn and an afternoon Sales Department meeting at the Diamond. When I add my daily routine of visiting each department, room inspections with the executive housekeeper, and the inevitable phone call from the brain-dead owner of the Hampton (who always asks, "How's bidness?"), my day is full. Aside from having to deal with the Hampton owner, I feel good about how productive I am going to be today. Now I just have to make it happen.

Better call the professor. There is no answer in Dr Spencer's room. It is early so I decide to wait and call later in the morning. While waiting, I review the updated payables list I received yesterday afternoon. The list represents the people I have been dealing with during this latest hotel recession. Most of the vendors are hard-working small business people who understand the problems of cash flow. They are gracious and willing to work with anyone who keeps them informed. In fact, they are a pleasure to work with, and the relationships that develop during the hard times are not forgotten during the good times.

The giant corporations and government people, on the other hand, offer no interest and/or leeway in accommodating people in financial difficulty. Some even act as if their less-than-average authority makes them decision-makers. I know it's not a problem I can solve but a constraint I have to live with. The problems with Accounts Payable (A/P) and Accounts Receivable (A/R) come and go as functions of the economy. When times are good, honest people pay each other; when times are bad, everyone is pressured to pay and, therefore, pressures others to pay.

Not having enough money to pay all the invoices can create a great deal of stress. Some of my people are not able to handle the pressure, and I have done all I can to keep them away from the calls and e-mails and take on the pressure myself. There are days, particularly the first and the fifteenth, when I wonder if I can take it anymore, when any email or blinking message light, representing people wanting money, makes me tense. Some of my days are filled with nothing but accommodating vendors' and service people's demands for money. I'm not dealing with guest satisfaction because I'm buried in money problems.

I find it amusing that management books ignore the problems with payables and receivables that arise during downturns. Often after having read one of the latest "answers to all of your problems" books, I am left with the feeling that the writer is using the "all other things being equal" approach to management. The issues of payables and, for that matter, receivables are almost as important as motivating people to work hard. When a hotel faces money pressures, tension fills the air. People are stressed, and with stress comes anxiety. Yet these same people pull the hotel out of the tough times it faces.

People are a wonderful resource to have, difficult at times, easy at others. Why?

I know that getting better results means understanding why people behave the way they do, and such an understanding must start with my own behavior. I decide to think about that while I'm working out today. This is cardio day, so the only concentration necessary is putting one foot in front of the other for over four miles.

7:00 A.M. Time to walk the restaurant. I see a few regulars and say good morning to them. I stop and engage in small talk with the guests that I know want attention, particularly from the General Manager. In a matter of seconds, they are happy and I can move on to the next person or group. A rule is to never interrupt a business meeting. I can acknowledge the person with a nod and keep moving. As I am about to leave, I turn and see Dr. Spencer sitting in a booth reading the morning paper.

I walk over and notice he is reading *The New York Times*. I greet him. "Good morning, have you had breakfast?"

"Yes, about forty-five minutes ago."

"I just called your room and thought you might be in the shower."

Spencer smiles and replies, "No, I'm an early riser."

"I have a question for you."

"Shoot."

"How did you come up with your approach for helping organizations get better results? Was it just putting together a lot of good ideas you've seen over the years or what?"

Spencer smiles. "That is part of it. I studied under two professors who influenced my thinking. One was H. R. Smith, the other Fredrick Bates. I try to be a logical, rational person who believes in gathering all possible information before making a decision. However, at times I found out that was not possible."

"So, how did you do it?"

"I took the work of Smith, the behaviorist, and Bates, the sociologist, and combined them in a format I can use as a leader."

YOU SHOULD KNOW

While necessity is the mother of invention, we all get to determine what is necessary.

"Well, I'm glad to see it paying off for you. You ready to get started?"

"Let's go."

With that, we get up and, after briefly talking to the host and the servers, we move on to the kitchen where things are in full swing. The kitchen has responsibility not only for a complete breakfast buffet but also for special menu orders and breakfast meetings for groups using the conference rooms.

The group meeting today is a state-sponsored class on pool maintenance. Each hotel is required to have a certified pool operator. To be certified, individuals responsible for pool maintenance must attend classes each year and pass an annual test.

The seminar lasts two days, so the meeting also brings some room business. I find the instructors and ask if there is anything they need.

They tell me that they enjoyed their night's stay and that the meeting staff did everything they asked. I turn to Spencer and smile. He nods and follows along.

8:05 A.M. We walk through the other meeting rooms, check the schedule of events for the day, and head back to my office. At the meeting room directory, I point out to Spencer that the hotel will be hosting three groups for seminars and lunch. There is a 130-plate dinner for tonight and a special breakfast buffet for the same group in the morning. That translates to 65 sleeping rooms with an average daily rate (ADR) of $159.50. This month is going to be good, much better than last year. The report this morning indicates we are running 12% ahead in occupancy and $13.23 ahead in ADR.

It's time to start planning how to spend the money that will be deposited today. The hotel recession has created the need to pay bills at least twice weekly. When things get better, the payables problem will disappear in a matter of months.

I wonder aloud if this month is the start of the turnaround. Spencer questions if this downturn will last longer than the others. It would be nice if the recession ends soon. These last two years have been hard.

I tell Spencer that my own people are worried about business, and their anxiety is reflected in their attitudes toward the guests. When people are anxious, they miss the details that make the guest experience special.

Spencer points out that if employees worry about the hotel's financial security, then they will begin to be concerned about their own financial security. I can expect this to result in a negative impact on their motivation and performance.

Just then Raymond walks into the office. Time to pay some bills.

"Raymond, like other long term people, was transferred from other operations when Matrix opened the Diamond. He is a professional and a good person. He is intelligent, reasonable, and has a good sense of humor. He's responsible for all of the back office functions of the hotel. He can tell me, within a hundred dollars, how much money is available to pay bills. He keeps up with all kinds of forms and documents that we need to run this place. If that isn't enough, he's responsible for deposits, credit card accounts, vendor lists, direct billing, and data entry for the P & L statements. Finally, the hotel's daily report and night audit have to balance every day; when there's a problem, people turn to Raymond."

Spencer says, "Raymond, all that makes me dizzy."

Raymond grins.

I continue, "All this seems difficult and stressful, but I think Ray loves what he does."

Spencer smiles, "It's interesting to note that what would seem a burden to one person is perceived as fun for another."

Raymond pitches in. "I'm very good at keeping track of the vast array of numbers, but I have no interest in dealing with the people problems of management. John, on the other hand, loves the challenges of individual behavior, but he hates the numbers side of the business. It's no fun for him, but he knows it's unavoidable."

I continue, "I have, for a long time, believed that people should find out what they love to do and then find someone to pay them for doing it."

"What if you are really good at doing something but hate doing it?" Spencer asks. "Then what? Hotel people, like most when first asked, cannot identify how they got where they are. However, with a little reflection, they realize they used this train of thought: They moved toward, or away from, certain positions and careers based on...well, let me show you. Let me just sketch this out quickly on this notepad."

He starts writing and in a few moments finishes. "Look at this."

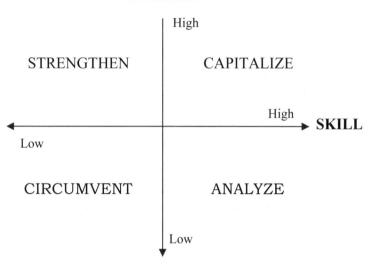

INTEREST

High

STRENGTHEN | CAPITALIZE

High
◄─────────────────────────► **SKILL**

Low

CIRCUMVENT | ANALYZE

Low

Spencer explains the model and how it speaks volumes about the human condition. He explains how most people are stuck in jobs they hate, requiring competencies that are over their heads, and how too many people spend most of their working lives doing something in which they have no interest. Moreover, these people will always be considered marginal and not worthy of advancement or special recognition.

"That may be true, but how do I get started finding out how the people I deal with feel about their career choices?" I ask.

"Actually, I've been reading about the latest method for obtaining that information," Spencer responds. "It involves using the SISP."

"The what?"

He smiles and explains. "The *Schilagi Interests and Skills Profile* (SISP) provides individuals with a reality check of their perceptions about various management positions in the hotel industry. The profile results reveal individuals' perceptions about their own interests and skill levels compared to others in the industry. The SISP also helps people decide if they are in jobs that match their skills and interests, and finally, and maybe most important, it helps individuals determine career paths that are consistent with their interests and skills."

"Where can I find out about this SISP thing?"

"Let me look for the website tonight."

"Okay, sounds like it might be useful to our management company."

"It could be because it helps place people in the right jobs. Plus, it helps when you're working with your people on career development issues."

"Does this profile take a long time to complete?"

"I don't know. I've never taken it. But I'm sure the website will give you the information you need."

KNOWING YOU

What were your results on the SISP?

It is almost 9:30 a.m. when Spencer finishes talking. Raymond, who has been listening intently, presents the report of revenues generated yesterday and the deposit that is to be made today.

"It looks like we will only have about $70,000 to spend," Raymond says, "and we have payroll, sales tax, the mortgage, and franchise fees to take care of before we even consider past due payables."

I can tell by his tone of voice that he is down today.

"Ray, we are about forty-five days away from the start of our good quarter. You know we'll catch up with almost everyone then."

29

He comments on the lack of business expected today and says he is worried about what the week will bring or not bring. While I share his concern, I know that to play "ain't it awful" is the worst thing I can do. If I sit around talking about all the bad things that can happen, Raymond will be a wreck by the end of the meeting. Although he is a professional, he could convey nonverbally his anxiety to his staff, and the cycle would begin. Department heads would get nervous and less understanding; the staff would feel the anxiety and begin to worry about their jobs. When that happens, the guests sense the lack of attention and soon feel uncomfortable. The domino effect of this seems wild, but the reality is that it could happen in just a few minutes.

When Raymond leaves, I turn to Spencer. "What would you do to keep him from worrying? Before you answer that, let me tell you a little more about Raymond. The fascinating thing about Raymond's behavior is that he is not concerned about money. He is independently wealthy now and will inherit even more. The question then is, if his anxiety is not a function of job security, what made him respond the way he did? What was his payoff?"

"His behavior might be centered on a payoff we can't readily recognize," Spencer says. "Often we get confused about the value of certain personal payoffs. Most of us tend to think everybody else values the same things we do. The fact is that one person's payoff may not be a payoff for someone else. It is difficult to put yourself in someone else's shoes, to think like they do, to know what they value in their jobs. Of course, there are ways to find out what the personal payoffs are for everyone."

The telephone rings, but I ignore the ringing. Spencer says, "I'm done."

I pick up the phone. My lunchtime appointment asks if he can change the time to late afternoon. I tell him that's not a problem. I turn to Spencer. "Speaking of stressful positions vital to the hotel, the front desk is a key to our long term success."

"Tell me about it."

"The front desk sets the tone for the entire hotel. Front desk people provide the guest with the first and last impression of the hotel. I consider that the most important factor in maintaining the business we have. After all, there are really only two major objectives to accomplish in any hotel.

"The first is to continue to seek and get new business and the second, and most vital, objective is to keep the business we have. I try never to lose sight of this because getting results is the name of the game in this business."

Spencer is listening intently, so I continue. "A sales department could be the best in the world, but if the hotel experience is not up to the expectations of the guests, they will move to another hotel. The result will be a constant revolving door of dissatisfied customers and a sales department that soon becomes discouraged. Again, the key is the people."

"People are always the key. Forget that and you end up in deep trouble."

"Hey, I know. That's why you're here. I'm always looking for ways to get better results. That's a big payoff for me. I'm hoping you're my ticket to some sustained improvement."

It is time to head to the gym, and I ask Spencer if he wants to come along. To my surprise, he says yes. He needs to go to his room to get some workout clothes, so we agree to meet in the lobby in fifteen minutes. I'm learning a lot with this guy and it's not only new but fun. I'm convinced the more someone learns about human behavior, the more questions arise.

It must be fun to have a job like his and be able to devote all your time to teaching and learning. Maybe I'll take the SISP to find out more about what my real interests are. I know I have the skill necessary to accomplish any task, so the important question is what my interest level is.

CHAPTER THREE

PERCEPTION IS THE ONLY REALITY

'Tis the perception of the beautiful, A fine extension of the faculties, Platonic, universal, wonderful, Drawn from the stars, and filtered through the skies, Without which life would be extremely dull.

George Gordon Noel Byron

10:00 A.M. As we drive to the health club, I notice the clouds are getting heavy and lower. The radio tells of impending snow with accumulations of up to four inches. In North Carolina, that is enough to hurt business. People will cancel room reservations, banquets, and meetings to stay home rather than fight the perceived danger of snow and ice on the roads.

Born and raised in Buffalo, I marvel at the reaction of people in this region to a little snow. And I always remember my first southern thunderstorm.

"I was driving through Virginia," I tell Spencer, "when the bottom fell out of the sky. I had never experienced wind and rain that hard. My first thought was that the world was ending. Then I assumed that just Virginia was going to be washed away. The rain was so hard that I pulled over to the side of the road, where I sat in amazement as cars with license plates from Virginia, North Carolina, and Georgia continued whizzing by."

Spencer laughs. "That's a great example illustrating that perception is the only reality. Those who kept on driving saw no great danger. Your perception, however, told you otherwise. You acted on that perception by waiting on the side of the road. The potential of danger seemed very real for you, so real that it became your reality. Our perceptions are real to us and become our only reality. That's why we act on them. Even when our perceptions are wrong, we act on them because they represent reality to us."

10:20 A.M. As we pull into the health club parking lot, Spencer asks how often I come here. I tell him about three times a week when I can. Then he wants to know what my payoff is from working out. I tell him that going to the gym is almost always a pleasure and that there are few occasions when the expectations I have about my workout are not met. However, when those rare occasions do occur, it's always because I did not perform. And when that happens, the stress that normally is gone by the end of the workout remains and may have even intensified. I ask him why that is. He answers me with a question, "Do you think that your stress level is a function of your perceived interest and skill levels or the perceived reward system?"

I give my often used intelligent response when I do not understand the question, much less know the answer.

"Huh? Could you speak English, please? I can't even make a wild guess what you're talking about."

As we park, Spencer says, "We haven't discussed that, have we? Why don't we hold it for later and give our brains a break."

As we stand in the lobby, he asks me to tell him more about going to the health club. I explain that my weight training days with my trainer of over sixteen years are always gratifying, if not fun. Roger, my trainer, knows more about fitness than anyone I have ever known. A true professional, he is ready, willing, and very able to push me beyond my wildest expectations. When that happens, all is right with the world. I can achieve a payoff that lasts two days—the first day because I know I've done my personal best and the second day because I am reminded by the soreness that accompanies building muscle mass.

When Spencer asks what I will be working on today, I tell him it is cardio day, which includes some leg lifts and squats but with the majority of time spent on the treadmill. Four and a half miles is my personal best but I feel like pushing for five today.

"The treadmill provides a great way to achieve the solitude I love. I believe that Anthony Storr was right when he wrote in his book, *Solitude,* 'The spark of creativity burns most brightly in a mind working in solitude.' Solitude is not appreciated enough in today's world."

Spencer acts as if he is interested. My sense is that he is more comfortable listening than talking. Hmmm, that's interesting because I tend to be somewhat the opposite. I mean, I do listen, but "show business is my life."

So, I continue. "The emphasis on groupthink and consensus management bothers me. We don't do things alone much any more. Look at how many things today have to be decided by a committee? It seems to me it is a great way to share the blame and eliminate the individual's accountability. Consensus management in my mind is nothing more than a lack of leadership. I think independence at work is a very important payoff, if not the most important, at least for me."

What are the other payoffs that make me want to do a good job? Do I really know why I work so hard every day? I even work hard at my fitness program. An interesting element in the gym is that some people treat it like a social club while others treat it like a gym. Everyone has different payoffs. Everyone has different reasons for behaving the way they do. As for me, I have to get results no matter what I am doing.

As we walk up to the registration desk, I hand the receptionist my car key. She gives me the stern look appropriate for someone ignoring the rules. She is new at the desk and believes that the big sign asking for your membership card is to be obeyed. I know that an exception is always made for me, but she doesn't. As Roger, my trainer and an owner of the club, has said, "He was with us before we were a club. He doesn't need a card. Besides, he would just lose it within a week anyway."

Just then, Bronz, the other owner, walks by and starts giving me a hard time about working out. The young woman notices the mutual teasing and hands me the key to my locker. While I do not want to make the young woman feel bad, I ask for another key for Dr. Spencer. She hands me one without asking permission from anybody.

As we walk away, I hear Bronz say, "Oh, that's John Battaglia. He's been around so long he's one of us."

"That was a good example of the confusion created when actual behavior does not live up to what is expected," Spencer says.

Will she continue to ask for membership cards or will she begin to let that slide? If she does start bending the rules, the result could be confusion down in the locker room. When a card is placed in a key holder at the front desk, the clerk knows that that particular locker is occupied. If there is no card, two people could be assigned to the same locker or assigned lockers right next to each other, even if the rest of the locker room is empty.

YOU SHOULD KNOW

Being a good leader requires an understanding of why people behave the way they do.

10:30 A.M. Spencer says he is going to warm up and then lift. I suggest that he warm up right here on the treadmill next to me.

"Why don't you call me Mark," he tells me.

Stepping up onto the treadmill next to him, I reply, "Oh, right. Mark it is." I select my workout program and press the start button to warm up. As the treadmill picks up speed, I turn to Mark and wonder aloud about what factors in a person's life influence the difference, sometimes significant, between actual behavior and expected behavior.

Spencer never seems to be at a loss for words when it comes to his field of expertise. He says that most people know what is expected of them in given situations—especially how they are expected to perform and how they should act when dealing with others. He emphasizes that the world is structured around a set of expectations about how people should think, feel, and act.

He continues by pointing out that what just happened is a good example. "The new receptionist had expectations and you deviated from them by not having a membership card and acting as if it did not matter. You were behaving the way you had always behaved, but it did not fit her world. That is one of the keys to understanding behavior. Everyone creates their own world and then goes about behaving rationally in that world, rationally as far as they are concerned.

"Most people, including managers and leaders, do not understand why people behave differently than expected. So they don't know what to do to get actual behavior in line with desired behavior or actual results in line with expected results."

KNOWING YOU

I know how important understanding behavior is so I spend time every day learning what makes people act the way they do.

Forty-five minutes and 3.2 miles later, it is time to move to the elliptical trainer. As I slow the treadmill down, I wonder what other factors influence the way I behave at work.

Just as I step off the treadmill, Victor walks by with a big grin on his face. Victor is one of the senior trainers at the gym. He actually does a little training here but mainly has responsibility for a big medical center training facility. He's a man with a quick wit and a smile most of the time. I have known him for years. Our standing joke is "Have you seen the only woman I have ever really loved?" Victor says that about every beautiful woman he sees. When he says it this time, he tells me the "only one" is one of Roger's new trainees. Mark and I laugh and walk to the Nautilus room a few feet away.

As we turn the corner, I exclaim, "Wow! Why is she coming here! She's all done!" From a distance, the woman is a nine plus. While obviously no one is perfect, she certainly comes close. As we watch, she is engaged in a serious discussion with Roger.

I walk back to the elliptical trainer to start the second part of my cardio day. This is easy and fun. I will work my upper body and legs for about twenty to thirty minutes. As I start pulling on the bars and stepping, I ask Mark, "Why would that young lady think she needs to come here?"

"Do you remember when we talked about Raymond and his payoffs? I did not stress how important payoffs are when you are managing and leading people to get results. In fact, the idea that people pursue personal payoffs is part of what I call the Performance Elements. We'll discuss that more, later."

"That makes sense. I've always believed in payoffs."

"Take the woman over there, the 'only woman you have ever loved.' We can think about what her payoff might be. Maybe it's maintaining her looks. Maybe she has worked very hard to obtain that look. Alternatively, maybe she sees faults that no one else does."

11:45 A.M. Pushing harder, I am counting the tenths of a mile and calories when Roger walks up and says, "You wanted to see me?"

"Yes, tell me what that young lady wanted to talk to you about."

Roger smiles. "Everyone has asked the same thing. What do you think she wanted?"

I reply quickly, "She wants to just maintain that look."

"Wrong!"

"What then?"

"When she came for an evaluation and I said she need not do anything, she was disappointed."

Mark chimes in. "Actually, her payoff is to improve her looks. That's why she was disappointed with your response, Roger. She wanted to hear something— anything, large or small—that she could work on to improve."

Roger looks at Spencer admiringly. "Okay, I see that. I think you're right."

I introduce Roger to Spencer and tell him a little about Spencer's work.

"I'm always amazed," Roger says. "Just when you think you understand people, you run across something you would have never thought of. Intriguing, isn't it?"

"John, here is a woman you should hire," says Mark.

"Okay, I won't argue with that," I reply, laughing.

"Whoa, John, calm down. Think about it. This woman has a high need for achievement. She is looking for anything that will help her improve. She doesn't react negatively to criticism. In fact, she seeks it because she knows knowledgeable criticism can be a path to improvement. You're the same way, John, or you wouldn't have me hanging out with you, right?"

I nod.

Mark continues. "Think about all the people in your hotel. How many of them welcome feedback, how many seek it out, and how many see it as an opportunity to improve versus feeling hurt or offended or getting defensive?"

"Sounds as if you know my people better than I do. Good point you're making. It is rare to find people who have a burning need to improve. How do I hire more of them?"

"Two things. First, you have to make it a top priority. Second, you have to learn how to do it."

"Top priority I can handle. Are you going to teach me how to do it?"

"John, as the old country song says, 'You got the money, I got the time.'"

I snicker then smile broadly. I like this guy. He is definitely a straight shooter, not afraid to let me know he is after my money, but he has substance. Everybody in the hotel industry would agree we need more people like him working with us. And he's funny, too. Everybody needs to have some fun at work.

Roger is laughing. When we calm down, he gets serious again. "She will soon be at a point where genetics will play the most important role in her improvement."

"Did you tell her that soon things would be out of her hands?" Mark asks.

"Yes, but she wanted a program anyway."

Mark smiles as if he is getting ready to have some more fun. "Okay, guys, that tells you she has a strong internally activated personal payoff, or IAP."

"Wait just a minute. A what?" I laugh, wondering if this is going to be some kind of academic nonsense. Spencer is not fazed by my doubting tone.

"Okay, John, internally activated personal payoffs are much stronger and last much longer than externally activated payoffs. Do you believe you control your destiny, the things that happen around you, that happen to you? Those are internally activated personal payoffs.

"Or do you believe that forces external to you, like the stars, control what happens to you? People who believe they have no control over things blame everything and everybody when something goes wrong. They never have to take responsibility for their behavior."

My head is spinning. "Why have I never heard of this before? It makes perfect sense. And I can think of a couple of people that fit the externally activated personal payoffs profile exactly. And you're right. They are bad news."

Spencer nods. "And, John, because you have internally activated payoffs, you probably have the foolish notion that you can develop such people so that they will stop blaming and start accepting responsibility. Right?"

I put a stern look on my face and try to say with my most serious tone of voice, "Dr. Spencer, have I told you how much I hate you?"

I want to learn more. "About the young lady over there who wants to improve on her near-perfect self, explain how you know she is internally activated."

"It's simple. Roger told her things would soon be out of her control, the role of genetics and all that, but she wanted a program for improvement anyway. That's because she believes she is in control."

"So you take one sentence, just one, and from that you know she has internally activated payoffs?"

"I'm no genius, John. You can learn to do it, too. It's not what she says; it's the meaning you attach to it that is important."

"So you're going to teach me how to do that?"

"Well, I'm going to try."

I have another question. "What about a person not willing to do an honest reality check? How long will she work at something that is almost sure to fail, and how will she feel when she realizes at some point that there has been no improvement?"

"Once she realizes she can no longer improve her body, no matter how hard she works at it, she will either lower her expectations, which she will do reluctantly, or she will be constantly disappointed."

YOU SHOULD KNOW

Negative payoffs are as strong a motivator as positive ones—and some believe stronger.

"When will her expectations match the reality she's facing?" I ask.

"Hard to say, but it will take a long time for her, given the importance of improvement to her and her IAP. One thing is certain. Until she does a reality check and faces that reality, she will be a very frustrated woman."

I wonder how I'll get a handle on all this stuff. I'm aware that, as good as all of this is, we are only moving on the edge of ways to improve motivation, and therefore performance, at the Diamond and, in turn, results.

Talking to Roger and Mark has slowed my pace and I start getting anxious about getting back to the hotel. I ask Mark if he is ready to call it a day. We have worked out for about an hour and a half. A good day's work and the payoff has been received, just as I expected, with the added bonus of learning some interesting concepts that I simply have to follow up on and apply. I know with Dr. Spencer that I am on the right track. At this moment, all seems right with the world.

As we drive back to the hotel, I wonder aloud to Mark about what influences the way I perceive my world. What are the things that make up reality for me? Moreover, who or what creates the expectations for my job?

"What do you think creates the expectations for your work world?" Mark asks.

"There are expectations about my job that fill volumes. For one, there is the franchiser who has committees that sit in their corporate offices and constantly change or add expectations. There is a rule change or addition almost every month. A few of the people in corporate who are trying to justify their jobs make up standards and regulations that are dropped or completely altered after they fail."

Spencer stops me. "Great example of negative payoffs—somebody giving you something you don't want."

"We all struggle with it, but it's part of being in the hotel industry. The new 'corporate' ideas from one particular franchiser have become a joke in the industry. These ideas are destined to fail or be changed in a matter of weeks. Sometimes their GMs just ignore the latest so-called great idea and within a few months, it is forgotten by everyone. However, I also know some GMs who follow all the new rules of this franchiser, no matter how stupid."

"True to form. When people receive negative payoffs, they respond in the usual ways, as you've described. There is frustration and complaining. Often people come up with their own payoffs to counter the negative ones, like having a little fun making jokes or ignoring something or someone, which can be a very positive payoff for some people. You wouldn't be in that category, would you, John?"

"Who? Me?" I answer with mock innocence as I laugh. "Okay, Dr. Spencer, you're just making guesses about my behavior, but you've been right every time. How do you do that?"

"John, it isn't magic, believe me. I've just trained myself to do it. Anybody can learn if . . . you want to."

KNOWING YOU

The odds of guessing a person's payoff and being right are not very good. Do you continue to guess or use your own payoffs as the standard?

"Sometimes when an incompetent franchise area director comes by," I continue, "I find ways to pass him off to someone else in the hotel."

"Sure, we all avoid people who give us negative payoffs whenever we can."

"Never thought about it that way, but we do. Life's too short for a lot of negative payoffs. Anyway, the area director changes so often that we have an inside joke about calling each by number rather than trying to learn names because none of them are around long enough.

"The latest 'help' from the corporate office was number three and that was within eighteen months. Predictably, her focus was not on the same thing as the last director we had."

Dr. Spencer nods. This guy really listens well and never says anything unless it is loaded with substance. I wonder if he can even carry on a conversation that is not related to his work.

"I realize that I do not expect all the ideas from corporate to work," I say. "It's not just a case of NIH or 'not invented here.' In fact, I dislike people who will not give an idea a fair chance unless they come up with it themselves. The owner of the Hampton is that way. On the other hand,

44

my management company, Matrix, is—for the most part—good at listening to all suggestions or recommendations."

"Tell me about your company."

"It's a good company. They take the time to know their general managers and department heads. Time after time, when people leave to try other companies, they ask to come back. The policy is that if you leave Matrix on good terms, you can apply to come back whenever you want. The longevity of most of their corporate personnel is impressive, particularly in the hotel business."

"Why does the hotel industry have such a high turnover?"

"It's not just turnover; it's burnout, too."

"Let's talk about that later."

"Okay. One of the reasons Matrix is such a good company is that almost everyone there understands the 'bad owner' problem. They devote a considerable amount of time to keeping guys like the Hampton owner away from the hotel staff."

"What would you say is the result of the behavior of Matrix?"

"That's simple. Everybody likes working for a company that is well managed, a company that cares, that makes its people feel valued. Motivation and performance are high. Everybody wins. In other words, everybody is pursuing personal payoffs and, for the most part, getting them. It's a great place to work."

"Makes sense to me."

"Mark, I have another example. When a GM has a problem, the management company is there to help. One example is with the annual budget preparation process. Matrix takes into account all the factors that affect the budget. The process is not the frustrating version where the management company makes the owner feel good for the one month of budget preparation and then forces the GM to explain to the owner for eleven months why the budget has not been met. This is a huge thing for a GM."

45

"What happens when the latter occurs?"

"The GM and the staff soon fall into the discouraging attitude of 'there is no way we can make this happen, no way to meet the budget.'"

"This is touching directly on the Performance Elements. John, which of the three elements would you say this situation represents? And which of the three elements of a Reality Check would you say that situation represents?"

"I'm embarrassed to say that I haven't read enough of your book to be able to give a proper answer."

"That's okay. There are three elements in the Performance Elements. We've talked about one of them already—payoffs. Another one is the perception people have about their skills and interests. That's the one coming into play here.

"When GMs have a budget that is impossible to meet, the tendency is to say, 'No way to make this budget; I don't have the skills to pull that off. I can't do it.' And with this conclusion comes a feeling of helplessness. Motivation sags. People give up. They give half-hearted effort at best. The result is that their performance lags behind what it could be. When people do not have enough confidence to perform the tasks, nonproductive things happen. Individual self-confidence is based on the perceptions we have of our own skills, not on the skills we actually have. Put differently, if I think I don't have the skills, my confidence suffers. That perception affects my motivation and performance, and that determines what kind of results I get. So you might say, in this case, that perceived skills determine motivation levels."

"Yeah, I see it all the time," I respond. "When people don't have confidence in their skills, they start going through the motions. They do the work, but it's never up to par. Then they don't get the payoffs they want. Like you say, I've seen people who have the skills, but they don't think they do. But their behavior is based on their perceptions, isn't it? Boy, when our perception is wrong, about anything really, that gets us in trouble."

"Exactly."

"I am amazed at the number of owners, management companies, bankers, and investors who prefer the Disneyland approach to budgeting. These people, the ones not on the front line, want to live in a financial fantasyland as long as they can. I can't understand why facing reality is so frightening to so many of them. Puzzling, isn't it?"

"In the budgeting example," Spencer explains, "the problem is that people are looking only at the short term. They are willing to suffer in the long run if only they can avoid a conflict with owners at budget time. People who hate confrontation find it a huge payoff to avoid conflict, and they will avoid it at any cost. Their goal is to avoid pain today and worry about tomorrow."

"Well, everybody is different; that's for sure. Some of those differences I can accept and live with. Some are very hard to face on a day-to-day basis. All I know is that few people will continue to perform at their very best without realistic payoffs."

"Well said!"

CHAPTER FOUR

DIFFERENT PAYOFFS FOR
DIFFERENT PEOPLE

There is nothing man will not attempt when great enterprises hold out the promise of great rewards.

Titus Livius

12:20 P.M. As we pull into the hotel parking lot, I point out that the ivy has been trimmed and the Leyland trees have been leveled at twelve feet, all without my saying a word to the Maintenance Department. We have an agreement with the power company that allows the hotel to have the trees twelve feet high as long as we let them grow no higher than that.

As we get out of the car, Mark says, "I disagree."

I stop in my tracks. "Disagree with what? The ivy has been trimmed and the trees leveled. What's to disagree with?"

"'Without your saying a word'—that's what I'm disagreeing with," he says with certainty and authority.

"But I didn't tell anybody to cut and trim..."

"You did tell them," Mark interrupts, "but not with words. Somewhere in the past, you spelled out your expectations, making them clear to the Maintenance Department."

He has a point to make, and I want to hear it. I just hope he gets off the college professor thing when he tells me. "Okay, Dr. Spencer, you have my attention."

"Good. It comes from a basic principle. Communicating your expectations to your people is necessary, but that alone is not enough. You did something else, not with words but with your actions. I bet that the head of the Maintenance Department has learned that if he does not meet your expectations, he will hear from you right away. He also has learned that if he does what you expect, he will hear from you with a payoff of some kind, maybe nothing more than a smile and a few words of positive reinforcement. This is another part of the Performance Elements—people having confidence that their behavior will be rewarded."

YOU SHOULD KNOW

All behavior that is rewarded is repeated.

"I just don't get it," I say. "I tell you the ivy has been trimmed and the trees leveled, and you know all that about me and my maintenance manager. By the way, everything you said is true."

Dr. Spencer's confidence in his own skills permeates the air. I wonder if his confidence is ever confused with arrogance. There is, after all, a fine line between knowing and being a know-it-all. Put differently, he is annoying right now.

"If you have the proper knowledge, you can explain the why behind most things. The same is true for behavior, if you have the proper knowledge." I'm thinking "blah, blah, blah" and laughing inside.

As we walk into the hotel, I notice the clouds are even darker. I tell Mark we had better stop in my office and check The Weather Channel. He has a plane to catch the next morning, and I want to be sure he is not snowed in.

As we pass the front desk, Eric, a guest service representative (GSR), hands me seven telephone messages. One is from the gas company representative demanding a payment. Another is from the guest supply company with the message that they will not even deliver COD without payment of a past due invoice. The supply company has a monopoly on the products my hotel needs, and they treat everyone like dirt. There is a message from Matrix asking me to call, one from housekeeping, one from maintenance, and two from sales people.

Mark asks, "Do you always have that many messages?"

"Yes."

"Where does your ability to handle the pressure come from?"

"Part of my confidence comes from one of the payoffs I receive from working with Matrix. It is their attitude about my time. The president of the company told me when I was hired that no one would ever question how I spend my time."

"While there are the standard vacation and sick day policies, my only requirement is to let the office know when I am not going to be at the hotel for more than two days. That is a simple precaution to allow corporate people to check in with my assistant general manager (AGM) or whomever I have placed in charge. The unwritten but deeply rooted expectation is that I will accomplish the agreed upon objectives in a time and manner that is consistent with Matrix policy. When and how I do that is entirely up to me. And that is a big payoff for me— independence to perform at my own pace, using my own methods."

"By giving you independence, Matrix is saying, 'We have confidence in you.' Looking over your shoulder every step of the way would be their way of saying, 'We don't trust you to get the job done.'"

"Yes, and another payoff is that when I receive a message from the Matrix office, it never creates anxiety. I love that aspect of working with them."

KNOWING YOU

Your level of perceived skill, when tested by others, can be strengthened or diminished depending on your level of awareness.

"I know people who at first think that the idea of independence is terrific but fail dramatically when given the freedom to use their own system of working with people," I tell Mark.

"Giving people independence when they are not ready can result in failure, and then confidence plummets," Mark observes.

"I know people who consider that kind of freedom to be too much and hate the lack of structure in their day-to-day lives."

"That's a very good example of perceived skills driving results. In this case, perceiving a skill deficiency holds back results. Some people want and need structure in their jobs. If they are given policies, procedures, processes, and step-by-step approaches, they feel comfortable and confident. They don't feel confident in their abilities to come up with their own ways of operating

51

and certainly not comfortable free-wheeling in uncertain situations. These people are not like you, John," Spencer laughs.

"You got that right."

"John, this business about perceived skills and how they affect confidence is important. We have already talked about it as one of the Performance Elements. Unfortunately, most people do not recognize its impact on motivation and performance and, consequently, on improving results."

"That makes sense: no skill, no confidence." Spencer starts to interrupt. "Slow down professor, let me talk." I hold up my hand and continue, "What I meant to say was, when people perceive they do not have the needed skills, their confidence suffers. And the snowball rolls. No confidence, no motivation. No motivation, no performance. No performance, no results."

I am beginning to understand why Spencer makes the big money. He shows you the dynamics of motivation but in a way that helps you clearly see and feel the importance and impact of it. Now that's valuable!

As we walk into my office, I comment, "I know a number of hotel management companies that are more than willing to provide all of their people with daily marching orders. In fact, just last week I talked to a former AGM who was working for a company that required daily meetings that often lasted two hours or more. Why would a company require daily, not weekly, but daily meetings?"

"The leader of that group does not have confidence in his people. He believes he is smarter than they are and that he can make better decisions than they can. He perceives his skills as being strong and those of his people as being weak. So he has tight controls, puts his imprint on every decision. He trains his people to obey—to do what he says, when he says it, and not to question anything. He robs people of their creativity, their initiative, and their motivation. High performers leave. Mediocrity prevails, at best. And that's my last sermon for the day."

I laugh. "I doubt that."

Mark laughs, too. "So the need for control is so great that the company is willing to have their employees quit thinking. Those willing to stay just go along with whatever they are told."

I am on a roll. "No creativity, no enthusiasm, and no payoffs except a paycheck. I couldn't work with companies, or owners, or corporations that do not offer independence as a payoff."

"Wait, you just said that some people couldn't handle independence. Are you now falling into the trap of thinking your payoff works for everyone? Maybe you should consider this undeniable truth: Everybody is different."

Duh! I know that—however, maybe not as well as I should.

The voice of the weatherman suddenly grabs my attention. Snow! The forecast is for snow starting tomorrow morning and continuing through Sunday. I know it will change four times in the next two days: not that the U.S. Weather Service is that inaccurate, but being less than a hundred miles from the mountains of North Carolina makes forecasting a bit tricky. I hold back on getting excited about the snow. It is easier to wait until it actually starts, although I can't keep from smiling at the thought of a big, beautiful snowfall. And the fact is that my people will be talking about the potential for snow for the rest of the weekend.

My high school friends from Buffalo laugh whenever I talk about missing the snow. They remind me that what falls in North Carolina is "Hollywood" snow—white stuff that is here today and gone tomorrow—while on the other hand, they have black, nasty ice and snow that hangs around for weeks or months.

Some people love the snow and even the ice, while others find it to be an anxiety-producing event and can't wait for it to be over. Another example of a key point about human nature: Different people have different payoffs. The potential for different payoffs is incredible—and that is for the simple stuff. What about the more complicated reasons for people's behavior? How do you get a handle on those?

I started the day wondering what my meeting with Mark Spencer would bring. Here it is a little after lunch and I'm excited about better understanding Spencer's concepts of behavior, motivation and performance, and improving results. This guy is smart.

I still believe that I need to know what makes me behave the way I do before I can understand the behavior of others. Now that Mark has explained what he calls the Performance Elements, the answer is beginning to take shape. Wait. Did he explain all three? The first is people pursue personal payoffs. The second is...how did he say it? Oh, yeah, perceived skills and interests determine motivation levels.

The third one is something about rewards. Well, remembering two out of three isn't bad.

Maybe during the snow on Saturday, I'll have a chance to read his book.

The restaurant is just starting to slow, and the 1:00 meeting group is filing in when we get there. They are late, but since they will be eating in the Atrium, the flow of people will not be a problem.

It's time to make some telephone calls. Most of the people I need to talk with will be back from lunch, or in the case of the West Coast, a morning coffee break, by one fifteen. I tell Mark I will be reading and answering emails before making telephone calls and suggest he get some lunch. All he has to do is just sign the check. I'll catch up to him after lunch.

After walking Spencer to the door, I check my email and find six new messages since late this morning. A quick glance at the emails indicates that more vendors and suppliers want money. Boy, this is a rough week; companies are approaching the end of the month and pushing for payment. There simply is not enough money to go around, and balancing the critical with the important is difficult. The critical bills are energy, telephone, and food vendors, while the important bills are franchise fees, guest supply companies, and other bills that will soon become critical.

I know that if I let the important invoices go unpaid long enough, they too become urgent. When that happens, it makes this part of my job seem like real work. I've always thought that something should only be considered work when you would rather be doing something else. And when it comes to payables, I would rather be doing almost anything else.

There is no one to turn to for help, so I start on the payment requests. Some turn out to be payment demands. It is hard not to take the comments of vendors personally. This is my hotel, and threats to it are taken personally. Demanding money as if the hotel has not been here and paying its bills for years is frustrating. Realizing that some people believe you are only as valuable as your last check makes dealing with them unpleasant, if not anger-inducing.

In spite of that, there is the payoff of holding back the wolves for another day. I know that the way occupancy is moving up each day means that things will get better. I am convinced of that, and that thought keeps me going. Mark would say that this shows that even a nasty job has a payoff, if you look hard enough.

Some vendors believe that the hotel economy is getting better, and they are working with me. Others want their money now, regardless of what the future may bring. One thing I do know about the latter group: They will not get the Diamond's business when occupancy improves. Spencer would say revenge may be a payoff. I know it is.

After reviewing the cash positions provided by Raymond and the requests and demands from the emails, I sit down to spend the money I have. Obviously, the gas company will not wait. They don't have to. The telephone company also has a stranglehold that should be considered a constraint and not a problem. Too many people waste valuable time trying to solve constraints. I believe you have to live with constraints and solve problems.

Once those are out of the way, I try to send most people some amount of money. Not paying the entire bill makes it more difficult for Raymond and his bookkeepers, but he understands the need to let vendors know we have not forgotten them. I finish the invoices as quickly as possible.

I head for the restaurant, finding Spencer talking to Tracy, our director of sales (DOS). I smile. No one can resist the charm, wit, and breathtaking beauty of Tracy. As I walk in, she is telling him about her struggle with the intense competition for rooms.

I sit down and listen while she explains the pressure she is under to fill the hotel and yet hold rates to the budgeted average daily rate (ADR). Mark listens and does not interrupt as she continues with story after story of her sales people giving the hotel away.

When she stops, she looks at me and says, "I met Dr. Spencer Wednesday night and I was telling him about my situation." She turns and says, "I have to go, Dr. Spencer. It was good to meet you and thanks for listening."

After she leaves, Mark asks me, "Do you have a good relationship with all of your people?"

"I think so. Why do you ask?"

"Tracy did not stop talking when you walked up. Do all of your people feel that comfortable?"

"Yes, I think so, although there are times when they get upset with me."

"When do you think that occurs?"

"When we have a problem with goals."

"Tell me more."

"Well, take Tracy, for example. We've been trying to solve the problem she mentioned for the last three months, the problem of her people giving away the hotel just to get business."

"Why would they do that?"

"Because we've had a decline in occupancy for the last two years, and while it's improving, it's not back to normal levels."

"And what are you doing to compensate for the lack of occupancy?"

"We have regularly scheduled sales meetings and go over the prospects and confirmed business. I'm reviewing the weekly call reports and dealing with the sales managers on future business rates."

"Do you not think Tracy is capable of doing that?"

"Sure, she can. It's just that the Sales Department really needs the attention now."

"And she can't do that?"

"She could, but right now I want to be involved."

Spencer smiles and says, "So, if it's not really important, you let Tracy run the Sales Department, but if things get tough, you step in."

"Well, if you put it that way, it sounds like I don't trust her to do the job."

"How would you describe what you are doing?"

"I'm just trying to provide some leadership."

"And after business gets back to normal, you will let her have her department back?"

"Look, Dr. Spencer, in the real world things..."

We both laugh out loud. I have reverted to the old saying about "you never had to meet a payroll" that so many people use when confronted with a leadership mistake.

Mark says, "Well, you recognize the problem. Can you pinpoint the exact element we need to work on?"

"Payoffs?"

"No, but there are only two more."

I laugh and ask him to tell me.

"What you have done is question her ability, not only to her but to all of the people in her department. They have to wonder if you are running the department. She now feels as if you do not value her, that you do not trust her to do her job, that you are undermining her authority, that you think she is not a good leader. Her perception about her skills diminishes, her confidence is shaken, and she is angry that you are doing this to her."

"Wow. What can I do?"

"Maybe you should ask her what she wants you to do."

As we leave the restaurant, Mark tells me that while I was answering emails, he changed his flight to this afternoon. The forecast is changing so rapidly that he really needs to get back to Atlanta today. I tell him that I'll take him to the airport and we can talk on the way. As he leaves for his room, he says he will call me when he is ready to go.

I walk to the Sales Office and find Tracy going over some call sheets for today's meeting. I sit down and say, "Tracy, have I been taking over your department?"

She looks surprised and answers, "Yes. I feel as if I'm just preparing reports for you."

"I didn't intend to do that."

"Well, my people believe they report to you."

"I'm sorry. I just wanted to help."

"You have helped the department's sense of direction, but now no one looks to me for guidance."

"Boy, I sure didn't want to do that. Dr. Spencer pointed it out to me just now. Why didn't you say something?"

"I tried, but when you got set to move forward without me, the best thing to do was get out of the way."

"I'm sorry, Tracy. I think you're really good and didn't intend to reduce your role in the hotel's turnaround."

"I know, but you have."

"Look, I have to take Dr. Spencer to the airport now, but we will correct this mistake, my mistake, ASAP."

"Okay. Let me know what you want me to do."

"Thanks, Tracy. I will need your help." I go to my office feeling terrible. Amazing how unintended consequences taint the intended results. I plan to ask Spencer about this on the way to the airport. Just then he calls and tells me he's on his way to the lobby.

We leave for the airport a few minutes later. As we pull out of the parking lot, I tell him about my brief conversation with Tracy.

"Do you have confidence in Tracy's abilities?" he asks.

"Absolutely. She is one of the best in the business."

"Why did you take away her authority?"

"I didn't realize I was doing that until you pointed it out."

"Well, what do you think you can do to fix the situation?"

"I don't know."

"Sure you do. Just think about the Performance Elements and do a Reality Check."

"I'm not ready for that yet. What are the chances of my attending one of your seminars?"

"I don't have any seminars for the hotel industry scheduled as of yet."

"I'll come to any of them, and I want Matrix to attend after I do."

He looks at his calendar. "My next seminar is in two weeks in Washington, D.C., for the Department of Transportation. It might just be perfect for you. I do the basic concepts the first day and then get industry specific in the second day. You could come that Tuesday and leave after the first day."

"What would it cost, so I can tell my company?"

"It will cost you half of the regular cost since you will be leaving after the first day. However, I will email you with the price Monday."

"Great. If Matrix doesn't want to pay, then I'll come on my own."

"Here is my terminal. Thanks for the ride and thanks for the experience, John. I hope to see you again."

"Thank you for opening my eyes, and I will see you in a few weeks. Have a good flight."

As I drive away, I tell myself that this Reality Check stuff could really be something important. I know Matrix is interested in the continuing development of its managers and leaders. The question is whether I can explain the basic concepts enough to convince them to pay for me to go D.C. If not, I will take a couple of vacation days and do it on my own. Either way, I am soon going to know much more about Reality Check for Leaders.

CHAPTER FIVE

THIS WILL BE ON THE TEST

Habit with him was all the test of truth; "It must be right: I've done it from my youth."

George Crabbe

There isn't anything like the gentle push into your seat that you feel as a plane gains momentum. As Delta Flight #1130 to D.C. lifts off the runway, I start thinking about my next two days. I will arrive in Washington around two o'clock. The ride to the hotel will take about an hour, so I should be settled in by three thirty at the latest. The Spencer seminar is being held at one of the major downtown hotels. The program will start at nine o'clock tomorrow morning, breaking for lunch at noon, and ending for the day at four. I plan to catch the 9:00 p.m. flight back to Charlotte.

Checking in, I realize that none of the other participants will be staying at my hotel: They are all federal government employees who live in the D.C. area. The front desk people are efficient and friendly. I often think about what is more important in the check-in process, efficiency of time or effectiveness in making a guest feel welcome. To my way of thinking, most guests who feel sincerely welcomed will excuse minor problems. A highly efficient but cold GSR, however, could leave a guest thinking the hotel doesn't care.

My room is spacious, well-furnished, and clean. I turn on the news and sit down with my copy of *The Washington Times* that I didn't finish on the plane. Ten minutes later, I get a call from the front desk asking if my room is okay and if I need anything. I ask for a 6:00 a.m. wake-up call and hang up.

Looking at the room service menu, I notice that it has the standard high-priced, limited selections that most hotels offer these days. The fact is that room service is too costly to operate, and hotels do their best to discourage guests from using it. High prices and limited selections send most guests to the restaurant. Limited facility hotels have neither the room service nor the restaurant problems facing most full service hotels today.

Around four o'clock, I finish the paper and decide to go down to the lobby to look around. The front desk is being hammered with check-ins. The atmosphere has changed from easy going and friendly to more efficient but less welcoming. People are being checked in, but I wonder if they feel as if they matter to the hotel staff. While I am watching the process from a chair in the lobby, Dr. Spencer walks in.

Actually, he does not walk as much as stroll into the lobby. He seems oblivious to the commotion around him as he takes his place in line. From where I sit, he seems to be reading something. The line is moving very slowly. There is some confusion and the front desk manager is called out a couple of times. Spencer does not appear to be bothered by this. Actually, I have a feeling he is enjoying it and is doing more of his research on human behavior. Sure enough, when he gets to the front of the line, he starts chatting with the GSR in what seems a casual, relaxed manner. About five minutes later, a bellman is summoned and Spencer is given a key to his room.

As he tips the bellman, he notices me and walks over. "Hello, John, glad you could get here."

"Thanks Mark. I'm looking forward to tomorrow."

"It should be fun. I'm told there will be about twenty-five people."

"Do you care how many people are in your seminars?"

"Only if the number gets over thirty. That makes it a little more difficult to interact with the audience."

"What do you do when that happens?"

"I change my style of presentation—you know, more PowerPoint, faster pace."

"Which do you prefer?"

With a smile, he replies, "I like the smaller size for the learning experience that I get and the bigger size for the money."

"What do you learn?"

"Well, I learn about the specific business and the challenges associated with each business."

"That has to be interesting. Who are the people coming tomorrow?"

"They are mid- to upper-level administrators from the Department of Transportation."

I smile. "How interesting can that be?"

"Well, I won't know until Wednesday when we get into the details of what they do. However, regardless of the operation or service, the problems of motivation and performance will be the same. And I can help them find solutions and get better results, regardless of the kind of results they are looking for."

"So you believe your Reality Check will work for any organization?"

"Absolutely."

I laugh. "So why aren't you rich?"

"I am," he laughs.

With that, we each head our separate ways. I know he doesn't like to socialize, so a drink or dinner is out of the question. Besides, I have some reading to do. I want to be as prepared as possible for tomorrow's session.

KNOWING YOU

Do you recognize when people have different payoffs than you do? Do you respond?

The wake-up call the next morning is a typical, computer-generated, cold, indifferent phone call designed to get you out of bed, period. I try to thank the computer voice and realize there is no need. I order breakfast, retrieve the *USA Today* off the door handle, and take a shower. Just as I finish shaving, my breakfast arrives. I have almost two hours before the seminar begins and decide that I will review what I know about Reality Check for Leaders after I dress.

I know better than to try to find a good news program in the morning. Even with seventy plus channels, the news options range from light, boring fluff to just plain stupid. I read the paper while I eat, then dress and head to the restaurant to observe the service and think about what Spencer has said in his book.

I reread much of the book last night and thought he had some great ideas. The book is obviously written by a bright intellectual and will be a valuable tool to all people who aspire to leadership excellence. I wonder, however, if the average working managers will want to take the time to understand what Spencer is trying to say. Do the seminar participants receive the book ahead of time? I'll find out soon.

The restaurant at 8:00 a.m. is as busy as the D's, with one notable difference—suits. Almost everyone eating in the restaurant is wearing a suit. Both men and women are dressed in business attire, in contrast to the almost self-conscious informality of some of today's corporate people. Whatever one's thoughts about our federal government, they sure dress nice.

I read my notes and look around to observe the table service. The servers move about as if they have been well trained. There is no confusion, and each helps the others when things get too busy. I ask for coffee and get a smile. These are well-trained, friendly people. A manager couldn't ask for more. I sign my check and head to the meeting rooms.

As I approach the convention/meeting area, I notice other people headed in the same direction. The meeting space must be about ten thousand square feet. That is enough to add room nights to the hotel but not so big as to be a burden in slow times. The area is first rate, with almost new carpet and lighting that reflect good taste and functionality.

The room is set up in a horseshoe seating style with a flip chart, chalkboard, and screen.

Four people are already in the room, and I walk up and introduce myself. I find my name card and take a seat. As I put down my book, I realize that no one else has one. I put it back in my briefcase and get a cup of coffee in the back of the room.

By 8:50 a.m., all the name cards have been taken and people are milling around talking to one another. I am the only outsider and keep to myself. Just then, Spencer walks in and heads straight to the front of the room. Boy, this guy really does not like chitchat. As he enters the room, people go to their seats. He sets his material down and quickly glances at some of his notes. He then looks up and greets the room with a warm smile.

"Good morning," he says, and we are off and running. "Before we start, I want to introduce you to a friend of mine who will be sitting in with us today. I did not want you to think he was a spy from the Office of Management and Budget." That gets a laugh and people acknowledge my presence with a smile or nod.

"Today we will deal with the basic concepts of Reality Check for Leaders. We will look at what makes people tick, what makes them behave in ways that are different from what you expect and hope for, and how to change their course to perform better and improve results. It's not magic or mystic. It is a realistic and workable approach to dealing with people. Tomorrow we will apply the concepts you learn today to your specific situations. By the end of our time together, you will have an approach that you can use in all of your dealings with people either at work or at home. Now, before we begin, does everyone know everyone?"

There are a number of people who don't know each other, so Mark does the tell-us-your-name-and-what-you-do thing. When he gets to me, I say, "My name is John Battaglia, and I am the general manager of the Diamond Creek Inn in Charlotte, North Carolina." There are a number of "can you get me a room?" comments, which GMs hear all the time. I smile and say, "Sure, give me a call."

Spencer glances at his notes again and begins the session. He explains that he conducts research on the subjects of motivation and performance, management, and leadership. "I teach people how to get better results without having to threaten or intimidate people. If you are not interested in improving your personal results, this seminar is not for you."

I have seen only one side of Dr. Spencer up to this point: laid-back but serious. His other persona has some real intensity. We have just been put on notice that this is to be a no-nonsense seminar. If you are not serious about learning what he is here to teach, you should leave.

"My research is done in colleges and for-profit organizations and when I travel." He continues, "The most helpful research often comes on the road with strangers. People tell you anything and everything because they know they will never see you again. I have for a long time thought that honesty is a function of pending distance. Did you ever notice that people who have known you for years open their hearts and souls to you when they are planning to move out of your city or even your neighborhood?

"For example, yesterday I was having dinner in a restaurant in New York. My server was an attractive forty-something and, boy, did she have an attitude. Her anger, or something, was obvious before she said hello. I smiled and said, 'Bad day, huh?' She glanced over her shoulder. I followed her eyes but did not see anyone. Turning back to me she said, 'So what's new.'

"Well, if that is not an invitation to talk, I don't know what is. Most of the dinner crowd had already cleared out. She wanted to talk. I wanted to listen.

"So, I responded. 'I had a job like that once. Hated it. What's going on here?'

"She said, 'How much time you got?'

"'I'm in no hurry, killing time before going to the airport.'

"She looked over her shoulder again and said, 'My boss treats us like dirt. He gives me no respect. Do the least thing wrong, and there he is, complaining. Never a nice word. But he is consistent; treats everybody the same.'

"I knew the type already, had met his kind of leader many times. In fact, there may be his type right here in this room." There was a nervous laugh and Spencer went on. "I looked at her and explained, 'He uses negative payoffs in an attempt to motivate. People learn to behave the way he wants so they can avoid getting something they don't want, in this case, his griping and complaining.'

"She nodded her head and said, 'You got that right. Everybody here does work hard to avoid that complaining.'

"'The problem with your manager's approach is that it tends to work. He gets what he wants and that reinforces what he is doing. However, it only works in the short run. People get fed up with that kind of behavior and leave, especially the high performers, because they can.'

"'Huh, I never thought about it that way.'

"I was curious. 'So, why are you still here? What is the payoff? You must be getting something you want.'

"'Well,' she said, 'for one, I like the customers, mostly business people, and they tip good.'

"'So how much longer are you planning to stay here?'

"'Not long. I'm looking. It's easy for good people to find a job.'

"Now it was my turn to say, 'You got that right.'

"This conversation illustrates a simple, yet monumental, point. Everyone knows it intuitively. However, it is a point that seems to be buried, hidden in our subconscious, collecting dust, unused, its value going to waste. The point is this:

PEOPLE PURSUE PERSONAL PAYOFFS

"Yes, people pursue personal payoffs. Let's look first at the word 'payoffs.' It just wouldn't make sense to pursue losses, not knowingly. Sure, with hindsight, we all have pursued losses, but not intentionally. Now, let's look at the word 'personal.' If people appear to be pursuing anything other than personal payoffs, it is only an appearance. Anything else being pursued is a means to an end, and the end is a personal payoff. Why would anyone ever pursue a payoff that is not of personal benefit? That wouldn't make sense. The idea that people pursue personal payoffs is one of the most important concepts in understanding human behavior. This provides the basis for you to persuade, influence, and motivate people to work harder, perform better, and improve results.

"I've done all the talking so far. Now it's your turn. Here is the question: What have you learned from this story? Give me short statements and I will write them down."

As Dr. Spencer picks up a marker, I look down at my blank notepad and realize I have been engrossed in the story like everyone else. A thought hits me hard: Was this story really based on a restaurant in New York, or was this Dr. Spencer's way of sending a message to me? He was in my hotel recently, ate in my restaurant.

The server in his story sounds just like one of my top-notch servers. The boss in the story reminds me of my restaurant manager. That's it. I have a server who isn't getting the payoffs she wants now, and she'll jump ship as soon as she finds another job that will give her what she is looking for. And what does she want? She wants to work for a good manager. Is that too much to ask? No, it absolutely is not too much to ask.

The question is this: Can my restaurant manager change the way he manages? Now, at least, I understand why turnover increased after he came on board. Nobody wants to work with a manager like that. I wonder if my Food & Beverage (F & B) Director knows what his restaurant manager is doing? If so, why hasn't he done something about it? More importantly, why didn't I know before now what is going on?

By now Spencer has listed all of the points made by the group. As he summarizes the list, I read it with him.

1. If employees can't get the payoffs they want, they either move on or stay and become less productive.

2. What is a payoff for one person may not be for another.
3. Good people have options and they are the first to go if their positive performance is not rewarded.
4. Managers are the company's reward system.
5. Ignoring bad behavior is the same as accepting it.

The last item on the list really gets my attention. Maybe I have a problem manager in my restaurant. Sure, I can blame my F & B Director. But in the final analysis, I haven't been on top of things as I should have been. I've got work to do.

This seminar definitely isn't what I expected, but thank goodness, I'm here.

YOU SHOULD KNOW

Real leaders can say—my fault!

Dr. Spencer brings me out of my thoughts.

"Great job on the learning points you came up with here. This is a really smart group, every one of you, except maybe John."

Mark breaks into a smile as the group does a double take at his comment, looking at those around them with expressions that say, "Did I just hear what I thought I heard?" and "Who is John?"

Spencer starts laughing. I briefly stand, laughing too, and say with as much sarcasm as I can muster, "Thank you, Dr. Spencer, for that vote of confidence."

The entire group is chuckling now, a couple actually laughing out loud, probably thankful that Mark is not picking on them. He stops laughing and continues speaking.

"Just kidding. I wanted to see if all of you were still listening. Back to the list. I agree with every single item on there. We will take a closer look at several of them as the day progresses.

"My next stop after leaving the restaurant in New York was the airport to catch a flight down here. Happily, there were no problems getting through security. That got me to the gate thirty minutes before boarding. I took a seat, intending to relax and read.

"'How you doing?' The voice was so pleasant and friendly I was sure it was a friend. Looking over to my right, I saw a man I had never seen before. 'Fine thanks. How about you?' I responded.

"'Just great,' he said with so much enthusiasm that I knew he was either a salesperson, a lobbyist or a happy drunk. 'On my way to Washington, calling on several of my clients. Play a little golf, go to some nice restaurants, and get a few orders. Really looking forward to it.'

"'Sounds like you enjoy your work.'

"'Now that's an understatement if ever there was one. I love my job! Been in sales for twenty-three years and I've loved every minute of it, except for the year they talked me into becoming a sales manager. Man, that was torture.'

"Who has not heard of the story of the great salesman getting promoted to a manager's job he can't do?

"'Is there anything you'd like to change about your job?'

"'Whew, that's a good question. Less paperwork would be nice, but I really don't have any complaints.'

"'Sounds like you're pretty good at what you do.'

"'I was born for this job! That's the only way I can put it. Never miss my targets. Make more money than I ever dreamed possible. I tell you, life is good.'"

KNOWING YOU

*Imagine finding something you love to do and then having
people pay you to do it.*

As Dr. Spencer finishes his story, I make a mental
exit from the seminar, again, and find myself back at the
Diamond Creek Inn. A clear picture is in my head of a
young management trainee who has been on board for
about six months. She reminds me so much of the
salesman Dr. Spencer just mentioned, with her
enthusiasm and excitement about her job.

In a recent conversation with her, I remember her
exact words: "John, thank you for giving me this perfect
job." Now there is a person who is delighted with the
payoffs she is getting. That will change if I'm not careful.
Eventually she could end up in a position that falls short
in the payoffs department. I'll have to stay on my toes to
be sure that doesn't happen or, if it does, to know about it
as soon as possible and take some quick action.

Wait a minute. Wait just a minute. I have a
question. I have tuned Dr. Spencer out completely. He has
paused and is looking at me.

"Mr. Battaglia, did you want to say something?"

"I do. First, I want to know how do you do that,
know I want to say something when I haven't said a word
or raised my hand or anything? Or is that simply the old
teacher trick."

"I've been watching you. You stopped listening to
me about five minutes ago. And now you are back. Makes
sense that you have something to share."

"In one way, it seems difficult to use this truth, if I
can call it that, that people pursue personal payoffs. On
the other hand, I have a feeling that it is a great way to
prevent a lot of people problems or at least catch them
before they get out of hand. Could you comment on that?"

"I can see that you were thinking during that little exit you made. Yes, on the surface, it appears difficult; but before the day is over, I will show you that it is not. Your second point is right on target, too. The benefits are enormous. People are more motivated when they have a chance to get the payoffs they want."

I agree with him when he says that; this means their effort increases, performance improves, morale is better, job retention is strengthened, and results improve. Those are obvious outcomes with any good leadership approach.

I don't agree when he says, "Moreover, your job is easier and more rewarding when you let personal payoffs of others guide the way you manage and lead."

"Okay, let's take a break," Spencer announces.

YOU SHOULD KNOW

Leadership includes giving people what they want.

CHAPTER SIX

UNUSED KNOWLEDGE HAS NO VALUE

A little knowledge that acts is worth infinitely more than much knowledge that is idle.

Kahlil Gibran

During the break, Spencer leaves the room. I know he needs time alone to recharge his batteries. Cool. Nice to see a man that understands himself and takes care of his own needs so he can take care of others. We're having fun and learning at the same time, a rare and pleasant surprise.

When he returns, he walks straight to the front of the room and gets ready to begin. I eat the last bite of a bagel and scamper to my seat along with everyone else, fueled and ready to go, wondering what will happen next.

He is not following his book, not exactly anyway. Everything here seems easier to understand, more practical. Reading is usually the way I learn best, but I like what we are getting in this seminar.

Spencer begins the next segment. "If we can agree that people pursue personal payoffs, the next major point takes us back to New York. I talked to a waitress in a hotel restaurant. Then there was the conversation with the salesperson at the gate in the airport. I boarded the plane and took my aisle seat beside a young woman, early thirties. I was tired, so I buckled up, put my head on the seatback, and closed my eyes.

"Just as I got comfortable, the woman beside me cleared her throat loudly. Sleep was coming quickly when she started crying. I thought, 'Why me, Lord?'"

YOU SHOULD KNOW

Dear (fill in your name),

Please do not take personal, irrevocable responsibility for everything that happens in the world. That's my job.

Love,
God

"I let her cry primarily because that was all I could do. She got a tissue out of her purse, wiped the tears away—not being very careful with her makeup—and blew her nose.

"'Sorry about that,' she said.

"I was thinking about all the times I'd heard people say, 'Don't cry. Everything will be alright.' I looked over at her and said, 'That's okay.'

"She continued, 'I hate people who love their work.'

"'Oh, you must be interested in experiencing some S*chadenfreude.*'

"She smiled. 'What?'

75

"You know, deriving pleasure out of the misery of others.'

"No-no. I don't really hate happy people; it's just that I'm miserable.'

"What has she told us so far? Think about it."

The class starts giving their ideas about what they know from what Spencer has said:

1. She hates her job.
2. She does not know of a way out of this situation.
3. She is a very unproductive employee.
4. We should question if there are more like her in her company.

Now that seems painfully obvious until Spencer describes what happened next.

"She sits straighter and says, 'Well, I hate the job I used to love. My company promised me a number of rewards if I would work hard and accomplish some specific goals. They promised I would be compensated for my efforts and that a promotion was sure to come from what I was going to accomplish.

"'I worked really hard to pursue those objectives with the idea that I would be rewarded later. Slowly it has dawned on me that this company is just horrible. The more I ask about my promised payoffs the more they lie. As a result, I am now going through the motions while looking for another job.'"

Spencer pauses. "Good leaders always look for meaning."

I think, no, sometimes even good leaders just look for a way out.

"There is one other thing you know for sure. What kind of manager does she have? Although I am trying not to sound too harsh, the word 'worthless' comes to mind."

Spencer continues, "All of you know important things about this woman, a woman you have never even met. You are able to define her at least in terms of her work as a disgruntled employee.

"By the way, have you ever met a gruntled employee? I know, I know, it's an old joke, but it makes me smile."

Spencer reminds me of the Johnny Mathis song with lyrics, "like a circle in a spiral, like a wheel within a wheel, never ending nor beginning." That's what my brain feels like right now.

How many of my employees at the Diamond Creek Inn have those kinds of negative thoughts and feelings bottled up inside them? More than I think, probably. I know a few who may. But I don't know for sure. I don't know who these people are or what is holding them back. I don't know how much it is affecting their performance or their contributions to results. Well, there's a lot I don't know—a lot I definitely need to know.

Spencer walks to the front of the room waiting for us to respond. The way I see it, that's what he is getting paid to do, make us think.

Spencer elaborates on the idea that behaviors that have payoffs are repeated. Take bad behaviors. Reward them and you will see them again. When you withhold rewards for bad behavior, they will disappear. I disagree with him here because I believe that adding negative payoffs is a much better way to deal with bad behavior. Some people need to be hit on the head with a two-by-four just to get their attention. The same is true for the behaviors you want. Reward them and they will be repeated. Fail to reward them and they will eventually disappear.

He continues, "This woman sitting beside me on the plane, can you picture the path she has taken from the time she started this job to where she is now?

"In the beginning, she worked hard and performed well but was not rewarded. Then what happened? Rewarded behavior is repeated.

"Behavior that is not rewarded begins to slip away and eventually disappears. This is happening to her. She has given up on her payoffs and her company. How many people do you know that just do what is absolutely necessary and no more? Professors call this minimally acceptable behavior. Leaders call this goof-off behavior.

"Another potential winner turned loser by the organization's reward system. Once people understand the reward system, they will behave very rationally, at least in their minds.

"Not only is she affected, but her behavior affects others. There is no way she can hide all that is stored up inside her. People working with her have seen a change in her motivation, her effort, her performance, and the results she produces. The changes have been considerable and very noticeable. If her manager wonders what is going on, he is an idiot; and if he knows, he is unprincipled. Again, behavior not rewarded soon disappears."

KNOWING YOU

Most people with work experience have faced various levels of negative company reward systems. Think back.

"We have all been denied the payoffs our performance deserves, and we have fought back in some way. This is normal. Everybody faces this at one time or another. The way you fight back is a function of your character. I suggest that if you have not received the payoffs you expected, your first priority is to accept that fact. This woman has not accepted reality. As a result, instead of just being mad at what has happened, she finds herself in a rage. Instead of being sad, she is depressed.

When she says, 'I don't know what to do,' she really means, 'I am in a panic as to what to do.'

"I'm sorry I've wandered away from the topic, but I feel it's important to know what you should take responsibility for doing. All of us must do a better job of providing people with their payoffs when their performance deserves it. Decide what you want from your people, tell them, and then reward them when they give it to you.

"So, what do we know? First, we know that people pursue personal payoffs.

"Second, we have emphasized that rewarded behavior is repeated. The third and final element takes us back to the observations made on my trip from New York yesterday.

"When I arrived at the hotel, I went immediately to the front desk to check in. The line was four deep. The guest service representative, a very pleasant young man, worked frantically trying to process everyone as quickly as possible. The line moved slowly. The GSR definitely had a haggard look, and his stress mounted by the minute. He seemed a little lost. One of the check-ins was nonverbally impatient, another vocal and rude. The GSR went behind the front desk and returned with his manager, who went to the computer and quickly handled matters. The manager appeared annoyed and spoke in a low, harsh tone to the GSR before returning to his office.

"I stepped forward when my turn came. The GSR gave me a professional smile and said, 'May I help you?'

"'Some guests can be a real pain, can't they?'

"His sigh of relief was followed by a real smile. 'Definitely. Bosses, too.'

"'I'd like to talk with you for just a minute.'

"'Okay.'

"'Tell me, what is going on here? Why the confusion?'

"'To be honest with you, I don't know what I'm doing. One person quit yesterday; one got fired. So here I am. I was only in my second day of training, definitely not ready for this.'

"'When do you think you'll be ready?'

"'Never. Computers are not my thing. Working with people is my thing. But I have to work. I'm going to school and need the money. They said I looked like a front desk person. What does that mean? Hire somebody for the way they look and not care about anything else? Doesn't make sense to me. Oh, well.'

"'So, are you going to stay?'

"'Too busy to look for another job right now.'

"'So what about this job?'

"'That, I know. I'll be frustrated because I'll never feel comfortable with the computer, but I'm good at dealing with people, especially the ones who are impatient, rude, and complain a lot.'

"'Then what?'

"'I'll do just enough to get by, not get fired.'

"'How long will that work?'

"'For a long time, I hope.'

"'How will you keep your boss from knowing what is going on?'

"'He is a complete idiot and I can manipulate him. Act as if I enjoy the work. Pretend he is a real winner. It's easy when you're smarter than the boss.'"

Spencer pauses and asks us, "Okay, what's going on here?"

He looks at each of us. The group responds with silence. How many of my employees are like the GSR in Spencer's story? I can see lots of blank stares, lots of wheels turning. Maybe everybody else is thinking the same thing. Maybe some are seeing some of this young man in their own employees.

YOU SHOULD KNOW

Your people can play with your mind. Just because you are named the boss doesn't mean you are in control. David Campbell said it best when he wrote the book, If I'm in Charge Here Why Is Everybody Laughing?

"The point is this," Spencer continues. "If people don't have the confidence to do the job, they will not perform as well as they otherwise could. The best you can hope for is that they will meet minimum standards. Is that enough? More likely, they will not perform well at all. When people do not have the interest or the self-perceived skill to do the job, they procrastinate; they work at the things that they are comfortable with rather than what needs to be done. The amount and quality of productive work they do decrease." In big letters, he writes on the whiteboard:

INTERESTS AND PERCEIVED SKILLS –
Determine the motivation to perform.

"When people don't have confidence in their ability, not much good happens. But where does the confidence come from? There is a simple answer. It is based on the perception of one's own skills. If people perceive that their skills match the task at hand, they have confidence and will push ahead toward achieving the results expected of them. If their perceptions tell them they do not have the skills, their confidence suffers and so do their motivation, effort, performance, and results. The conclusion is that self-perceived skills drive results.

"Perception of skills can be inaccurate. People often believe they have the needed skills and charge ahead on a job or task. A great example of that is the fact that when asked if they can jump rope for three minutes without making a mistake, almost ninety percent of respondents say yes. The reality is that less than five percent can actually accomplish that seemingly simple task. When dealing with self-perceived skills in the work place, people may have the tendency to overestimate their actual skill sets because they want particular payoffs. If their perceptions are accepted by their leaders, then somewhere along the way, they both discover they were wrong. When this happens, employees' confidence drops, causing drops in motivation, effort, and performance. And managers are faced with fixing problems that they created.

"Sometimes people have the perception that they do not have the required skills when, in fact, they do. In this situation, which is the most prevalent, the manager must first know about the self-perceived skill sets. There are a number of surveys available that can help a leader understand their employees' self-perceptions about their skill levels.

"In the hotel industry, for example, the *Schilagi Interests and Skills Profile*—or SISP—is a great way to determine how your employees perceive their various skill sets. A determination of employees' self-perceptions can make the difference between motivated people and unproductive, unhappy people.

"Skill confidence problems can greatly impact performance. People who don't know the difference between waiting for reality to change and choosing to change it themselves do not stand up and say, 'I can't do this.' It can become really difficult when we hide our perceived weaknesses from our bosses and, in extreme cases, from ourselves. It makes us feel weak to confess, 'I don't know how to do this.' How many of you in this class right now want to ask a question but are afraid of the consequences? Afraid of exposing a weakness? We might get punished in some way, maybe even get fired. Most employees want to ask for help but are protecting, maintaining, and enhancing their self-images to the detriment of the work that has to be done. How often have you heard, 'I understand,' and found out later they really meant, 'I understand half of what you said'?

"How many of your direct reports are not performing as well as they can because of skill confidence problems stemming from their perceptions of their abilities? And how is this affecting their motivation to do their jobs or at least one major part of their jobs? Are you in this situation?"

Spencer pauses and I immediately begin to think about my situation. Sure, there are some parts of my job where my mind tells me I don't have the skills for this. The whole motivation and performance arena is one of them. That's why I'm here at this workshop. I'm doing something about it. Why can't everybody do that? Take responsibility for developing their skills. Well, that's not fair. I can decide to take time off from work to do it, can get company money to do it, but my employees don't have that luxury. Okay, this is an issue I need to address right away.

I look around the room. Some people have their heads down. Others are staring straight ahead. Some are doodling on their note pads; a few are writing fast and furiously. I wonder how productive this time is for them. Some people don't understand that a simple rule applies to doing something about the problem:

YOU MUST DO A REALITY CHECK

While he stands and watches, most in the group are busy writing down what needs to be changed, I think. He continues.

"Any questions?"

Spencer calls on a man with his hand up sitting toward the back of the room. He is frowning and looks confused. "I was wondering," he says. "This seems so complicated."

YOU SHOULD KNOW

If leading were easy, everyone could do it. Then it would get very crowded at the top.

"Complicated? Maybe," Spencer responds. "But I think it depends on what you know. In terms of payoffs, certainly, people are different. A payoff to one person may or may not be so for another. Some employees like freedom and independence while others prefer jobs that are highly structured. Some people have a high need for praise and recognition; others need those much less. A payoff for one may even be a punishment for another. For example, one person may view a promotion as the ultimate payoff, yet another will fight tooth and toenail to stay in the current position. We could make an endless list that illustrates differences in people when it comes to payoffs.

"So, even though people do want different things when it comes to payoffs, one thing holds constant— rewarded behavior is repeated; behavior that is not rewarded diminishes and eventually disappears.

"When it comes to perception of skills and the confidence that follows, yes, people are different. We are not created equal. We have different abilities and different capabilities to develop our skills. Moreover, if we are not careful, we end up in jobs that do not match our skills. Everyone is different.

"I cannot emphasize it enough—people simply are different. Interesting though, isn't it, that so many managers treat everyone the same? Some managers use a participative management employee involvement approach with everyone. Others assume money is the number one motivator for everybody. Still others believe everybody wants to be part of a team. Many managers give the same detailed instructions to everyone or hardly any instructions at all."

He continues, "In spite of obvious differences in people, many average managers and poor leaders use the I-know-the-right-way approach to management. Why is that? The answer is simple: Bad managers promoted because of seniority, policy or simple attrition and who want to believe they have gotten to where they are with their leadership style. And they continue to believe, if it's not broken don't fix it—even if this runs counter to everything we know about people."

A big man on the front row throws both hands up in the air. He looks like a professional football player: about six feet four inches tall and every bit of 250 pounds. His southern drawl makes me chuckle—only to myself, of course; I'm too young to die. He says, "Tell me then why we should fix it. What can Reality Check do for me?"

Mark laughs but people in the room are a little nervous. The same question is on everyone's mind. Why should I learn something new and different and therefore potentially destructive, if what I am doing works? Spencer picks up on that and says, "For those of you who want to know what the payoff can be for changing your approach, I can list a few right here." He writes on the board, reading them aloud as he does so.

1. The task of leading will become fun.
2. You will be able to get more goals accomplished with people.
3. Your people will appreciate the honesty in the work environment.
4. You will probably make more money.

I look around the room. Heads are nodding and hands are up. I notice that people are adding their personal payoffs to the list. We want some answers. He smiles, leans against the wall, stands silently, and looks around the room. The more he stands, the more people talk. I realize they are trying to get their payoffs on the written list. Interesting.

Spencer steps close to this giant of a man, checks the time on his watch, and looks up to the group as he says, "Time for lunch."

As he leaves the room, I notice that food is waiting for us at the back of the room. He has no intention of staying here and being barraged with questions.

I need a break from this academic stuff, but these concepts keep popping up. I'm wondering how to put these ideas to work at the Diamond Creek Inn. Application is always the hardest part. It all seems so simple, sitting here and listening to what appears to be the undeniable truth. Going home and using it will be the real test.

When Mark comes back in to get the afternoon session started, he looks ready to go. I realize why we had an hour and a half for lunch instead of the usual one hour. He wanted to plan the afternoon based on what he heard this morning.

"There is one other point we need to discuss, then we'll do some group work to let you start applying what you are learning. Let's go back to Kennedy Airport and the salesman I talked with at the gate before boarding the plane. He said two things that are really important. He said, 'I love my job.' Then, a few minutes later, he said, 'I was born for this job.' When that combination occurs, you have a winner on your hands and you are a third of the way there."

He has just put another bad thought in my head. How often have I taken good, high-performing people, moved them into other jobs—maybe even promoted them—only to watch things fall apart? Now I can see it was my fault. Spencer is exactly right.

This reminds me of Rosie, our bell captain. I think he loves his work and is perfectly suited for his position. He has administrative and leadership responsibilities and handles those very well. In fact, all of the promotion offers he has received have been based on his obvious leadership skills. We've tried to promote him. But he keeps turning us down. Why?

KNOWING YOU

Can you admit that you don't know? To others? Really?

The silence startles me. When I look up, Spencer is staring at me. Uh oh, I've done it again.

"Welcome back, John."

"Thank you, sir. I've been watching my own mistakes pass before my eyes. Could I be excused to call my shrink? I need some therapy." That sends a nervous chuckle across the room. Guess I'm not the only one learning something about my current leadership abilities.

"John, what is happening to you is normal. It's part of the learning process. You already are seeing how you are going to apply what you are learning here. Congratulations. Do you have something else to say?"

I continue. "I was thinking about what happens when we put people in jobs they don't like or jobs they aren't equipped to handle. Some get disenchanted and leave, right?"

"That's correct."

"Others get fired for poor performance."

"Yes."

"And some stay, do the least possible to get by, and maybe even become troublemakers. Left alone, they will drag down the results of those around them."

"John, you are exactly right. Would you like to just come up to the front of the room and teach the class for me?"

This gets a good laugh. I consider it praise. Spencer is following his own advice—reward what you want from others. I admire that. He continues.

"What Mr. Battaglia has done is paint a clear picture of what happens when we do not get people in the right jobs. Let's look at the other element in this sequence, that of interest levels.

"Not enough can be said about the impact that an individual's interest level has on performing a particular task. When people have a deep interest in their work, one of the biggest payoffs they get is the satisfaction from the work itself. This payoff does not come from someone else. People give it to themselves. They reward themselves every day simply by doing work they love.

"Think about it. If you put people in jobs that match their skills with their interests, you prevent so many problems that interfere with getting the performance you want.

"On the other hand, when people don't like their work, their willingness to perform decreases. That results in less effort. As a consequence, performance is affected and objectives are not met. Why? It's because these people are not in the right jobs. It's not always possible to make perfect matches, but we all can recognize when we're wrong and do something about it."

I am about to ask how we find out what a person's skills and interests are when I remember the SISP, the survey that measures just that. I check my watch. If I get an earlier flight, I can get home and start to use all of this good information. Whoa! Who knows what else I might learn before the seminar is over? Back to Spencer.

"You're going to do some application work in groups in a few minutes. I want to prepare you for that by summarizing where we are, giving you some priorities, and adding a thought or two. Here we go.

"An important thing for you to remember is the Performance Elements:

1. People pursue only personal payoffs.
2. Rewarded behavior is repeated.

3.   Self-perceived skills and interests
     produce/determine results.

Together, these help you understand human behavior and
enable you to lead people to improve results. When you
know these, you will be able to match people to the right
positions and motivate them to perform at high levels."

Spencer stops his lecture and starts giving
instructions about the group work. The purpose is to
prompt us to think about situations in our leadership
positions where we could apply what we are learning
today. We spend most of the afternoon doing this. It is
helpful, hearing the views of others and verbalizing my
own thoughts. I get some good questions that help me see
a few things more clearly. All in all, it is productive time.

Mark calls us back together and has each group
report on some of the major points we've discussed. He
listens and writes a few things for each group.

"Nice work in your teams," he says. "You are
catching on to the content, and more important, you're
acting as if you are beginning to believe it will work for
you. That is a big step, believing it will work. Without that,
you will do nothing with what you have learned. As you
know, unused knowledge has no value.

"Let's wrap up the day by putting Reality Check for
Leaders in perspective. It is very simple really:
Understanding work behavior is difficult but not
impossible, and people who master the art of Reality
Check will be very good leaders for a long time in varied
circumstances.

"Remember that people can seem to enjoy their
work but, in reality, may hate what they are doing, or we
may think they want more money when they really want
more meaningful work. They may appear to be confident,
to have the skills needed for the job, when actually their
minds are saying, 'I can't do it.' People may not share

those differences with us unless we ask them to. Simply that, ask them."

I think he is talking about me now. Independence is very important to me, and I have been assuming everybody else wants it, too. I'll probably make that mistake again but not nearly as often. He has already helped me see that everybody is different. I know that intuitively, but I haven't been acting that way. I've been making far too many assumptions about people, and most of them have been wrong.

"We may believe we are providing the right payoffs for specific behaviors," Spencer continues, "but then again maybe not. We may think we know the organization's reward system but not the way our people perceive it. We may be certain we have our people matched with jobs perfectly when in fact we don't.

"The point is this: Perception is the only reality. Put differently, reality often is different from what we think it is. The way we see things becomes our reality. And that is the reality we act on. So, if our perception is distorted, we may have a problem."

YOU SHOULD KNOW

Everyone has a perception of his or her world and behaves rationally within that world.

"We have to perform a Reality Check to determine if our perceptions are correct, to see if our own reality matches what is actually real. For example, think of one person you lead that is not acting the way you expect them to. Do you have that person in mind? Now here are some questions you can ask. These become your Reality Check.

"Let's say you believe the three most important payoffs for this person are flexible work hours, autonomy to do the job right, and specific rewards when warranted by performance. Are you correct?

"You may believe you have done a very good job of rewarding this person when performance expectations are met. But does the person understand the organization's reward system? And is this person happy with the payoffs the system provides?

"Your perception tells you that the interests and skills of this person match the job. However, does this person feel the job is a good fit?"

Spencer takes a few moments to write those on the board:

REALITY CHECK QUESTIONS

1. Did you ask the person what their payoffs are?
2. Is successful behavior appropriately rewarded in your organization?
3. What are the skill and interest levels of this person?
4. Do they match their current position?

"Okay, are you getting the picture of how to do a Reality Check? Yes, I know. You're thinking 'I know that.' Be sure to avoid the trap of assuming that, if it is simple, it is unimportant. This has been the downfall of many leaders—failing to give attention to the simple things, the basics. The question is 'Are you listening?' We'll do some more work on this tomorrow."

Everyone in the group gets up and heads out in separate directions. I thank Spencer for the day and tell him I will be in touch soon about presenting this same program at Matrix. Then I head to the airport, anxious to apply Reality Check.

As the cab takes me to the airport, I can't help thinking about how Reality Check can help me in my job and my career. I see the payoffs as two-fold. One, I will be a better leader and I will get noticed by top management; and two, I will be the guy that brings Reality Check to my company, which will also get noticed. I can see a future in a corporate office of Matrix or some other management company.

I stop to pick up a paper, this time *The Washington Post*, and head for my boarding gate. It has been a great day, well worth the time, effort, and money.

CHAPTER SEVEN

BEGINNER'S LUCK OR THE REAL THING?

In business you get what you want by giving other people what they want.

Alice Foote MacDougall

I arrive in Charlotte around ten thirty Wednesday night and have the hotel van pick me up. Rosie, the captain and occasional van driver, is in his usual good mood. While I've heard he can be difficult to deal with, in all my years working with him, he has never been anything but professional. Sometimes he's quite full of life, but he's always professional.

I know of five promotions the man has been offered over the last eight years. In each instance, he respectfully declined. People at Matrix tell me he has been turning down offers for at least fifteen years. A Reality Check may not change anything, but maybe it will help us understand his behavior and keep us from constantly shaking our heads in puzzlement.

When I think about it, though, Rosie is a perfect match for his job in terms of skills and interests. According to Spencer, this is the ideal situation. Rosie just might be smarter than all of those people offering him promotions.

It's late and I'm tired, but I'm looking forward to using what I've learned to understand what motivates Rosie. He drops me off at the entrance. I thank him and walk through the lobby and lounge to say hello to some of the night people.

The lounge is just getting started and, after my long day, all I can hear is noise. The restaurant is closing and I ask Mary how we did that night. She says we did fine; we had 120+ covers at an average $61.40 per check. That's a good night for a hotel restaurant. In the restaurant business, it's table turns and average check that make or break a place.

I decide it's too late to even get near my office, so I head for my car. Tomorrow will bring new hotel problems and some chances for me to practice Reality Check for Leaders. I like the sound of Reality Check. It's easy to say, has a nice ring to it, and creates a little mystery, too.

I plan to prepare a presentation to Matrix about what I've learned. The information could be very useful, and I am anxious to try it out in real hotel situations.

I arrive back at the hotel at around seven thirty the next morning. Yesterday was good but long and took a lot out of me, so I've taken my time getting to the hotel. As I walk in, I hear, "Good afternoon, Sir," a good-humored comment about my always being there before the first shift starts.

Ken, the new front desk manager, looks surprised to hear the sarcastic comment. I bet he wonders why my people feel so comfortable with me. He says hello and asks to meet with me some time today. I ask if it's urgent, in which case we can meet now, or if not, I can come back after I look over what's on my desk. He says it can wait, so I go to my office.

What I find is a typical number of emails for a two-day absence, along with memos, snail mail, and notes from various staff people. Looking over the pile of stuff on my desk, there is nothing that strikes me as urgent. The payables problem is still there, of course, and staff questions have to be answered; but it's not as bad as I assumed it would be.

It's funny how blinking message lights and email counts make me tense. What I've started doing is answering them ASAP. Things are never as bad as I imagine. People react well to quick responses; and even if I cannot solve their problem immediately, they know I care about the outcome.

Dr. Spencer warned everyone about the problem of stepping back into our work environment and immediately getting caught up in day-to-day problems. He said, "If you believe Reality Check Leadership will help you, then you have to believe it's not adding to your normal workload."

The first opportunity comes when Raymond walks in and asks how the seminar went. I try to convey my enthusiasm for what I have experienced. He listens and, when I finish, he says, "I suppose you didn't save your receipts."

"Well, no, but I meant to. Here's what I have left from the advance I got." I give him about $130 and some change.

YOU SHOULD KNOW

Certain expectations can be ignored if you are good enough at what you do.

95

"Great," he says. "Thank God, Matrix understands your strange behavior because I have to send them a note that says, 'This is what's left.'"

"Sorry."

"Yeah, right. So here are the numbers, and I have a few requests from department heads."

We review the requests and the urgent payables, coming up with a plan to handle everything. With payables, sometimes it takes sending check numbers before vendors will even fill the order COD. Those vendors are the ones that know they have monopolies. The franchiser made a deal, and the supplier is the only source.

I often wonder why that is not a violation of some restraint of trade law. However, I have no say in the matter, so we have to play by their rules.

Raymond and I continue to work on payables and receivables for about an hour. When we finish, I have some phone calls to make, and he notifies the department heads that we are getting most of their supplies.

After he leaves, the first call I make is to the Vice President at Matrix. I ask for a meeting to talk about Reality Check for Leaders. We agree on Friday afternoon at the corporate office.

As I think about the meeting, I decide to do a PowerPoint presentation. I have two nights to work on it and will find some time today and tomorrow. Sometimes you just know an idea is good and have to go with your instinct. After all, instinct is just experience and knowledge combined to give one a sense of right.

I usually go with my instinct and have a good average. I know Reality Check for Leaders (RCL) is going to be good. And I want to be the one who shows Matrix the concept and sees a payoff.

KNOWING YOU

It is not enough to have a real interest in doing well; you must also have the skill set for the task.

The day continues uneventfully. By three o'clock, I find myself with some time to work on the RCL presentation. I will have about thirty minutes of the VP's time, so I have to punch up the presentation. If she is convinced that we should give RCL a try, it could mean that the entire company will hear what Spencer has to say. Just as I begin, Tracy, the DOS, walks in looking discouraged.

"What's wrong?" I ask her.

She replies, "My people will not listen. They say they are going to change the way they prospect for business, but they continue to use the same techniques that we know don't work. And I don't know what to do."

I immediately recognize 'I don't know what to do' as a potential problem. She is questioning her skill to handle the situation and her confidence is shaken. Okay, so what do I do? The pain on Tracy's face is obvious. What did Spencer say? I'm drawing a complete blank.

"Tracy, you are one of the best DOS people I've met. You run a good office and keep up with the details necessary to make the Sales Department productive." I remember what Spencer said about perception and that if Tracy is concerned, then that is what I have to deal with. There are some facts about her performance as the director of sales that she seems to have forgotten.

"Your people respect you and seem to follow almost everything you say, so why the problem with this?"

"I don't know."

Things are slowly coming to me. When people perceive they do not have the skills they need, self-doubt takes over their thinking. When this happens, one

97

solution is to give them new skills. That's it. Maybe I do know how to help Tracy.

"What if we try a new technique I learned at a seminar just yesterday?" I ask. "It can't hurt and might provide you with an answer. Let me tell you a little about how Reality Check works."

We talk for about an hour. She asks a number of questions and seems intrigued by the idea of actually finding out what motivates people to behave the way they do. The more we talk, the more excited she becomes. I have to cut off our discussion because I promised Ken some time. We agree to meet again after I walk the hotel.

YOU SHOULD KNOW

Opportunities to apply what you learn are everywhere. However, most of the time the old way is easier—in the short run.

As she leaves, I pick up the phone and ask Ken if he wants to meet now or later. He says he has a few things to do and around five would be good. We agree to meet in the lounge. I try to meet in the hotel public areas whenever I can. The staff gets to see their supervisors meeting and working with the GM, the department heads seem more comfortable in a neutral environment, and I like getting out of my office.

Since I have a few minutes, I think about my presentation to the VP on Friday. I want to convey a sense of promise but not an overly pie-in-the-sky attitude.

She is an experienced operations executive who has been in the business for twenty-six years. She has witnessed "the latest and greatest" solutions to organizational problems come and go, so this presentation has to have a note of authenticity. What I've learned in dealing with her is that, regardless of the situation, I had better come to the meeting prepared to defend my ideas.

Anything less and I get my hat handed to me. The funny thing about it is that she tells people in the nicest way that their idea may not be the best she ever heard but to keep trying. Sometimes it takes two hours to realize they have been put down. The other interesting thing is that they also come away feeling it will be okay to try again with another idea. Most GMs like the process because she is willing to listen.

How best to convey Reality Check and the potential it holds? That is the major question for me.

I think about real examples but realize that I won't have enough time to use the Sales Department problem. Maybe Ken will have an issue I can use. I start laughing. Who sits around hoping to find problems? I feel like one of those MBAs with a bag of solutions looking for problems. What I need is a simple example of how Reality Check can work.

I get up and leave my office to walk around the hotel. I know that just walking through the place brings issues and problems to light. Some of the staff are more than willing to share their ideas with me. Others are there for the paycheck and don't want to make waves. They won't volunteer information that isn't requested. Finally, there are those who will attempt to tell me exactly what they think I want to hear. Those people are obvious and annoying.

Walking into the laundry room, I'm struck again by the heat and humidity. I've been in the hotel business for years, but the hostile environment in the laundry room always surprises me. These people can outwork anyone in the hotel. Fran has been with us for seven years and Evelyn for five. They work well as a team and can keep up with the highest occupancy levels the hotel can accommodate. The massive washers and dryers produce heat that can't be controlled by air conditioning. Big fans move the humid air around the laundry rooms.

Matrix has the corporate staff spend a week at one of the hotels they manage every six months. The purpose is to allow corporate people to experience what working in a hotel is really like. It's a great idea that lets corporate spend time with the people who make the hotel run. Moreover, it helps my people see that corporate personnel are not desk-bound idiots. Almost everyone has a good time, and Matrix people learn a lot about day-to-day operations. However, when anyone accustomed to an office environment is assigned to work in the laundry room, they usually fade within two hours.

Fran says, "I can tell business is better."

"You're right," I reply. "We have been doing better, particularly Tuesday and Wednesday nights."

"We had to come in Saturday, too, to cover for the race weekend."

YOU SHOULD KNOW

People can create a good environment under amazingly difficult conditions. What may seem very difficult for you is just another day for them.

"Yes, we were filled Friday, Saturday, and Sunday because the race was under the lights," I reply.

"I'm glad to see we're doing good."

"Thanks, Fran, so am I. And thank you for all you and Evelyn do."

She smiles. "You're welcome." Evelyn nods and smiles. She's not as comfortable with me as Fran.

I leave the laundry room and head to the sales office. Tracy is working on a sales and marketing project she calls a sales blitz; I call it the Concentrated Call Program (CCP), a program that brings a number of sales people together to visit potential customers in a selected area.

It's funny how concepts can be described in positive or negative lights just by the choice of words used to describe them—concepts like "concentrated call program" versus "blitz," or "inexpensive" versus "cheap," for example. My department heads joke about using the right words in a presentation, but I encourage them to spend time on selecting the words they're going to use. Sometimes great ideas are lost because of lack of preparation of the presentation.

That brings me around to my presentation on Reality Check. I need time to work on the concept, but for now my concentration is devoted to Tracy and her problem.

As I knock and walk in, Tracy looks up from her calendar and smiles. It's an understatement to say that when Tracy smiles, the room lights up. She has all of the attributes anyone could ask for in a sales and marketing director or DOS. She is intelligent, creative, and beautiful. In private, she says that her looks often get her into an office or meeting but her brains keep her there until the sale is closed.

Tracy loves the sense of accomplishment that comes with closing a deal worth thousands of dollars. She is paid very well and considered a star in her field. She has been with the hotel for five years. I sometimes wonder how many other jobs she has turned down. We long ago made an agreement that Tracy will tell me about any offer she is interested in exploring. So far, so good.

"Hi, want to talk now?"

"Now is good." I take a seat and she continues. "I'm working on a way to force my people to make cold calls."

"Why do you think you have to force them into making cold calls?"

"Some are frightened, some are lazy, and some don't know how."

"Tracy, let's look at the cold call problem in a different light. What if we examined it from the Reality Check point of view?"

"How would we do that?"

For about ten minutes, I explain to Tracy that looking at motivation from the perspective of the individual's perceptions might alter the way we think. For example, rather than setting up a work environment that forces everyone into the same working structure, what if we set up individual goals based on what Dr. Spencer calls the Performance Elements, which is a major part of Reality Check for Leaders? I summarize them:

1. People pursue only personal payoffs.
2. Rewarded behavior gets repeated.
3. Self-perceived skills and interests determine results.

"Let's start with their self-perceived skills," I suggest. "If your people think they don't have the skills to make successful cold calls, they won't have much confidence and that will hold them back. For example, of the six of you, how many are good at making cold calls and know it?"

"Three of us, and that includes me, seem to get results every time."

"How about the other three?"

Tracy thinks for a long while before replying, "Well, Bill is really good at telemarketing, and Rachel can really close a prospect on the phone. She can get a site visit out of one phone call."

"Who's left?"

"Henry."

"What can Henry do well?"

"Keeping our website up to date and working with the reservations department computer."

"Well, everyone seems productive, just not in the same way. Is there a way you could let everybody do what they do well and make this thing work?"

"I don't know. Aren't you supposed to treat everybody equally? The same way? Won't they get upset if I don't?"

My mind flashes back to the Spencer seminar and the major points he stressed.

Okay, I say to myself, you know the elements of Reality Check, so use it now.

"Do you think they are going to complain if you ask them to use their strengths?"

"I guess not, but we have always all done the sales bl... the CCP together. It builds morale." We both smile at her quick change in word choice.

"How much morale does it build if half the team dreads it because they know they're not good at making cold calls?"

"But if they tried, they would love the feeling."

"Tracy, that brings to mind another of the Reality Check elements. Just because *you* get a good feeling—a payoff—when you sell a stranger, doesn't mean everyone does. They may not want the same payoff you do. Besides, the negative payoffs of doing something they don't like to do can outweigh the good feeling of making a sale on a cold call.

"The last element deals with the way people are rewarded; their payoffs, if you will. For example, Henry is rewarded for being the Internet guru. The better the website, the more you praise him and the more confident he becomes in his ability. On the other hand, asking him to meet and talk to strangers when he barely tolerates the people he knows here is counterproductive. In other words, Henry knows the reward system will not give him the payoffs he wants when he is making cold calls. So, forcing behavior that does not match his payoffs does no good. For him or for us."

"I like that approach for Henry, but what about my other two?"

"Good question, Tracy. I think that's for you to figure out. Just remember this: Dr. Spencer helped me realize that everybody is different. Because of that, the idea is to manage to the individual. In other words, let people do what they do best, what they like to do, what will give them the payoffs they want. You can't always do this, but you can always try. You never know what you may make happen, if you try."

I can see Tracy's brain working, processing, absorbing the concepts of RCL. She's very smart, and it doesn't take her long. "Okay, what if I assign cold calling to the three of us who are good at it and use the others for backup and follow-up?"

"If you think that will work, go for it."

"Okay, I'll rethink all of this just to be sure. I'll find out what everybody is thinking, specifically the payoffs they want and don't want, the way they feel I reward them, and their perception of the skills they have for making cold calls. If I can do all that, I'll have a motivation system that will work!"

I just sit there smiling, thinking how long it has taken me to get to this point. But here I am, and that is all that matters.

Tracy says excitedly, "I think Reality Check for Leaders makes a lot of sense. Thanks for bringing it to me."

"Tracy, it will be a little harder than you think, but you're smart and I know you can make it work. RCL is going to help all of us."

"Will it work in all departments?"

"So far, I think so. I intend to find out for sure."

Tracy flashes that smile. "Well, I know what we'll be doing around here for a while, at least until it becomes part of our leadership style."

"Let me know what you come up with for all of your people and you regarding those three elements." I get up to leave.

"Oh, one thing you didn't tell me. How do I find out?" she says.

It is my turn to smile, "Why not ask them?"

She laughs. "Got me. I will get back to you soon."

"How about early next week after the staff meeting? Will that work?"

She looks as if that may be too fast, but I tell her she should stop planning the Concentrated Call Program for now and use the time to gather information on Reality Check for Leaders and her people.

I am pleased. This discussion, it seems, has gotten her confidence back on track. The personal payoffs she wants are within her reach again. I give the credit to her being receptive to trying something new. That is the mark of a true leader. I have a good feeling about her, about RCL, and about all it's going to do for us.

CHAPTER EIGHT

FACE TIME WITH THE VICE PRESIDENT

Great people talk about ideas, average people talk about things, and small people talk about wine.

Fran Lebowitz

    I leave Tracy's office and head back to mine. I want to work on my presentation to the VP. What is the best way to explain what I think is a great approach to leading people? I get a cup of coffee and pick up a legal pad. After reviewing my notes, I start putting together the presentation.

    The goal is for real behavior (what people actually do) to equal expected behavior (what you want them to do). The problem comes when real behavior and expected behavior are different.

Reality Check can help anyone understand why people behave as they do. It enables you to bridge the gap between:

1. Norms (the way people are expected to think, feel and behave), and
2. Acts (the actual way people think feel and behave).

RCL can get the behaviors you want and need to run a well-managed department or hotel operation.

I sketch out a diagram to show that RCL acts on the individual in a way that real behavior and expected behavior become the same.

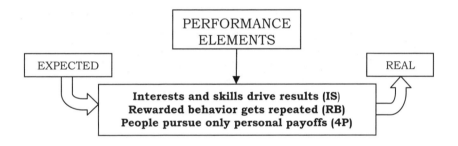

I often learn best when I simplify what I've been exposed to and convert it into something I can remember. I also know that the VP likes formulas and numbers, so I come up with this:

IS + RB + 4P = REAL BEHAVIOR

I plan to tell her that when people do not behave the way we expect, their behavior could be the result of three things. First, they may perceive their skills to be inadequate to perform as expected, which can cause a lack of confidence that holds them back. Second, if they are not being rewarded when they show the expected behaviors, they will conclude, "What's the use?" Third, they may not be getting the payoffs they want, and payoffs are the reason for everything. While all three of these elements sometimes can be determined by observation and discussion, often it requires additional time, effort, and thought.

Most people do not freely talk about their skill level problems or openly share their personal payoffs. Moreover, to complicate the process even more, they may just say what they think you want to hear. I plan on saying that RCL requires different leadership skills, not additional ones. This approach to understanding behavior does not add to a leader's work; it makes it easier. I will tell her that the first step in Reality Check is getting answers to the three vital questions. Without the answer to those questions, a leader is just performing inefficient trial and error actions destined to be unproductive in the end.

PERCEIVED INTERESTS AND SKILLS

Think back on the number of times people have said to you, "Don't worry; you'll do great," on a test, speech, or presentation. You probably thought, "Fine for you to say. You don't have to do this." The people you work and live with every day often face situations in which they think they don't have the skills they need to accomplish specific tasks. It's one thing for you to say, "You will do great on this assignment," when requesting their help; and another for them to believe they can do it. For example, if individuals are uncomfortable with an assigned task because they have never done it before, it is your responsibility to help them understand the process and maybe even help them develop the skills they need. In most cases, talk is not enough. Real leadership may mean educating people to perform new and sometimes difficult tasks. The adage that a great salesperson does not necessarily make a great sales manager is too often ignored.

The consequences of not matching the interests and perceived skills of an individual can be devastating to the department and maybe to the entire organization. Further, moving a great salesperson into a leadership role the person is not interested in can be even more detrimental to the department.

I remember a few years ago when a very long-term and loyal employee developed a serious illness that prevented her from walking. Because her job required a great deal of walking, I attempted to find her a place in the corporate office. She had been a bookkeeper in her past, and although the technology had advanced, I thought she could learn and adapt. In fact, I used those exact words, "Don't worry; you'll do great." The result was a disaster. She, for whatever the reason, never learned the "new" way of accounting. She took more and more time off and in the end left the organization. We subsequently found an almost insurmountable number of bookkeeping corrections that had to be made.

The fact that she had absolutely no confidence in her ability held her back and left her unable or unwilling to put forth the effort needed to learn her new job. I found out later that she hated bookkeeping and had no interest in a career that did not include her old position. She left our company, blaming others for her loss in the race between retirement and obsolescence. And I realized that sometimes you just don't have a place for those people in the organization.

Funny, isn't it, how our self-perceptions influence our behavior? The mother of a friend of mine used to say, "Can't never could." That's true. If you think you can't, you won't try hard enough to succeed. The thinking of people with perceived low skill levels is "Why bother? I can't do it." People with low interest levels think "Why bother? I don't care." With either perception, results are hindered.

I plan to tell Long, the VP of Operations, that by using the *Schilagi Interests and Skills Profile,* found at www.DirectionsForHospitality.com, we could go a long way in identifying the perceived interests and skills of our current and future people.

REWARDED BEHAVIOR IS REPEATED

I also plan to tell Long that what people believe to be the reward system in a company is the only reality for them. The idea that people create their own worlds and then behave rationally within those worlds is a vital part of their views of the reward system. I will mention that often what starts out as a benefit, over time, becomes a right and hence is no longer considered a reward.

The bottom line is this: Rewarded behavior is repeated; behavior that is not rewarded is not repeated. If people in the organization do not believe they will be rewarded for behaving and performing as expected, then no employee handbook in the world will change their opinions.

People learn from experience. The example I plan to use is the Hampton Inn. Matrix has been given a management contract; the employees are told that Matrix will be responsible for the reward system. Unfortunately, everyone knows that the owner interferes with the reward system at every opportunity and that his promises are worthless. As a result, good people start looking for an organization with a real reward system. Turnover is off the charts and the GM becomes frustrated and discouraged. The perceived lack of a reward system keeps the Hampton from excelling in its performance.

The owner, a man seldom right but never in doubt, has a reputation for always blaming others for his mistakes. Everyone knows this negative reward. What really hurts everyone's confidence in the stated reward system are his frequent visits to the property. Because he desperately needs attention, he shows up unannounced and takes two hours to tell the staff of his next "great plan" for the Hampton. He requests huge amounts of information that take up the time of the hotel staff and the Matrix corporate office and then never mentions the "great plan" again. People never are rewarded for all the extra effort they put in for the owner. Eventually they develop expertise in avoiding him whenever possible; also, they don't volunteer for anything. Behavior created by the lack of rewards spills over into everyday functions and results in decreased productivity.

I will suggest to Long that the Hampton could benefit a great deal by learning how the employees really feel about the reward system. By using RCL, we could learn how to improve a situation that is dysfunctional by its nature.

YOU SHOULD KNOW

Perceiving payoffs as unattainable slows performance down and keeps people from meeting objectives and producing results.

PEOPLE PURSUE PERSONAL PAYOFFS

As a final point, I will tell the VP that the expression "people pursue personal payoffs" (4P) seems simple enough until the concept is examined carefully. After listening to Dr. Spencer, I have come to understand that you have to be careful about jumping to conclusions and that what is a payoff for one person is not necessarily a payoff for someone else. What's more, the range of payoffs that individuals can want is as varied as their individual personalities. Payoffs can be warm feelings, security, money, love, family time, revenge, health, lack of stress, status, recognition, a sense of achievement, and on and on. Sometimes an office instead of a cubicle can be a payoff; sometimes it's a new truck or better tools that help people feel rewarded. You can never assume what someone's personal payoff may be, and finding out can get complicated.

The important aspect of this concept centers on identifying the payoffs that individuals have and working to reward them in ways that match what they really want. Make no mistake. Some people do want money, power, status, things, and stuff. Others, however, are not as interested in material payoffs as they are in experiences, a positive working environment, and recognition for achievement, to name a few.

Spencer told of an incident in which he was asked about his own payoffs. He stated that while some people collect experiences, he collects things. When dealing with him, you had better know that material things are a payoff. I believe Reality Check can help Matrix clarify the payoffs that people are looking for in their work.

The problem with finding out what people want as their individual payoffs is sometimes called the social desirability factor. Spencer explained that sometimes people express their payoffs in ways they believe you want to hear. It's the supervisor's job to create an environment that allows people to express their real individual payoffs.

YOU SHOULD KNOW

Offering people the wrong payoffs also slows performance and keeps them from meeting objectives and producing results.

The process of learning about payoffs is essential to the overall success of RCL. However, all three elements have to be considered together if the motivational system is to be effective.

I will tell the VP that I have already started using RCL with Tracy and that we believe it will benefit the Sales Department. I wonder aloud if that will be enough to convey my appreciation for Reality Check or if I need more information for the VP.

Spencer suggested asking as the easiest way to gather information about employees' motivation. The approach of simply asking makes it possible for the supervisor and employee to establish a working relationship based on a sound strategy for motivation and leadership. No longer will a GM have to guess about the motivation of his or her department heads. Instead, the GM can know what their payoffs are.

In my presentation to the VP, I will stress that the act of asking provides the information the GM needs to manage. Moreover, it can work for any manager or leader at any level. It's not easy to get people to open up and tell you what you need to know to be a good leader. But when you develop the mutual respect that comes from really communicating with your people, your role as leader becomes much more effective.

I stop writing and put the pad down. Time to leave my notes for a while and come back to them later. Funny how, sometimes, ideas that seem good at the time are not as impressive when reviewed later.

I decide to go online and check out the SISP profile Spencer mentioned—an interests and skills inventory that helps people determine if they are suited for specific jobs in the hotel industry.

YOU SHOULD KNOW

Learning is a humbling experience but it can be exciting and productive.

SISP is a way to get people in the right jobs. I remember in the seminar that Spencer said the most important thing leaders do is put people in jobs that fit them. That is what the SISP helps you do. I find the website, www.DirectionsForHospitality.com. The company, founded in 1974, has been consulting for hotels, country clubs, and other organizations (both profit and nonprofit) for years. They published the SISP after more than twenty years of experience in the hospitality industry.

The SISP was recently introduced to the hospitality industry in a conference sponsored by Phoenix Hospitality. The people who took it were impressed with the accuracy of the profile and how useful it could be in placing people in the right positions. They felt this would go a long way toward improving job retention, which is a continual challenge in the hotel business, and would strengthen leadership performance across the board.

I can take the profile online or go to a one-day seminar dealing with leadership and the results of my responses. According to the description I can expect that my results will confirm some things I already know and reveal some areas I need to question. The profile should take about forty minutes, and at the end, I will receive the results instantaneously. All in all, it looks like it could be a wonderful learning experience about one of my favorite subjects.

Now, I have all the factors clearly in mind and feel comfortable about my presentation to the Matrix VP. I have the facts, the formula, examples, and the SISP that will all help me in my presentation.

Leaving my office, I head for the front desk to meet with Ken. When I get there, he is in a heated discussion with a GSR. They both turn as I step into the doorway to Ken's office. I tell Ken I will be in the restaurant when he has time.

I walk to the restaurant and go to my table. While I am not in favor of having a table set aside for me, the restaurant staff wants to please me. This is their way of showing respect to the GM. My quiet compromise is that I never use the table during rush hour at breakfast, lunch, or dinner unless Matrix people are in the house.

It is eleven o'clock and very quiet in the restaurant. The wait staff is setting tables, vacuuming the floor, and generally cleaning up after breakfast. I sit and Cindy, the host, brings me a cup of coffee. As usual, she is pleasant and efficient. She was a server for years but decided to host after serving became too draining. She is our prize, and Matrix sends servers and hosts to her for training before allowing them to start at other Matrix hotels. Even the morning breakfast host at the Hampton came here to learn from Cindy.

I look at the paper and drink some coffee. There are times like this when I really miss having a cigarette. After all these years, the psychological pull is still there. Moreover, while it is not difficult to ignore it anymore, I am amazed at how long the dependency lasts—amazed at how a habit broken years ago still has a perceived payoff. Ken interrupts my thoughts as he sits down. I ask, "How's it going?"

"As you can see, not too well today," he replies.

"What's wrong?"

"Well, I'm new here and I'm not sure how much authority I have."

"Could you be more specific?"

"Well...," he hesitates, "I'm not sure how to say this."

"How about just saying it? How bad can it be?"

"Okay. The GSR you were kidding with this morning, Bob, has been testing me at every opportunity."

"And you're wondering if you have the authority to terminate him. Right?"

"Yes," he says, obviously relieved to have the words out.

"Well," I say, "you certainly have the authority to do that. I would, however, if I were you, look at Bob's personnel file before you make a decision. He has some good skills and has been with us for three years."

"So, I can't fire him."

"That's not what I said. I said you should make your decision based on facts, not on your feelings of being hurt."

YOU SHOULD KNOW

Good leaders use every bit of relevant information they can get.

"How did you know my feelings were hurt?" he asks.

"You just told me." I smile.

"Are you a shrink or something?"

"I'm a 'something,'" I reply, and we both laugh.

"Okay. What should I do besides looking at his file?"

"Well, here's what I would do. First, I would pull his file and set up a time to meet with him away from the front desk. Next, I would let him know that you want to give him a chance to continue here but not at the expense of the front desk staff's motivation.

"After that, I would give him some benchmarks to meet and let him know that he has been warned. Don't use my name because I want you to gain the respect and authority on your own, and you won't get it by using me as the hammer."

"What if that doesn't work?"

"Make it work. Why not think of reasons why Bob is behaving the way he is? In fact, go talk to Tracy about Reality Check for Leaders."

"Any reason to talk to Tracy is great with me." He catches himself and apologizes.

"Don't worry. Tracy knows she's beautiful and she doesn't have a problem with people noticing. You should know, though, that she's as smart as she is good looking."

"Thanks." Ken gets up to leave.

"Keep me informed daily of your progress, Ken. Nothing formal. Just a call or visit will do."

As he walks away, I think now I have two tests of RCL going. I sure hope this works. My payoff for this effort is the chance to present this to all the GMs working for Matrix. I like public speaking and I often joke about my big chance at "showbiz." I have invested a great deal of time and energy, as well as a part of my professional reputation, on this approach to motivation. Events have happened so quickly that I haven't really had time to consider all the consequences of my actions.

Now is not the time for self-doubt. I believe RCL will work, if given a chance; and if Matrix doesn't like it, I will use it at my hotel and try to use it at the Hampton.

The major problem with the Hampton is the owner. However, that might be an interesting test of the theory's effectiveness with constraints as well as problems. After all, an idiot owner is a constraint that a GM and the management company have to live with if they want the contract. I have heard that another management company terminated a contract with the Hampton owner and that a major law firm actually fired him. Why has Matrix put up with this guy? I have never asked before but think I may this time. His reputation could be damaging the company's business image.

As far as I'm concerned, I need to get back to basics. I want RCL to work, and I'm ready to sell my ideas to the VP at Matrix. I look forward to my meeting in two days.

KNOWING YOU

How much time and preparation do you put into key presentations? Don't tell me you wait until the last minute because it turns out better when you're under pressure...Please!

CHAPTER NINE

BACK TO THE DRAWING BOARD

*If at first you don't succeed, try, try again.
Then quit. No use being a damn fool about it.*

W. C. Fields

I eat an early lunch in my office and read my notes about RCL. The information will be compelling if presented properly. I'm convinced that RCL is not more work for a manager but another way of motivating the people who count. The line people in any hotel make the difference. If they're comfortable and happy with their environment, that attitude is projected to the guests. If the employees are not satisfied with their work situation or are confused about their responsibilities, then that attitude is also conveyed to the guests.

My meeting with the VP of Operations is set for 2:00 p.m. I plan on driving through Charlotte on I-77 north for about forty miles and then another thirty-five on I-40 East to the Stratford Road exit.

The Matrix offices are located in a three-story colonial building on one of the main streets in Winston-Salem, North Carolina. The drive should take me less than two hours, but I always plan for slowdowns and stopping on I-77. The Federal Highway program has been going on for three years with no sign of stopping. If I get lucky, I'll be early; and if there are normal delays, I'll be on time. It always makes me feel better to have extra time. There is enough stress in the hotel business without running late being added to the mix. I need a clear head for this presentation.

As usual, the VP—never one to waste time or money—has scheduled one-on-one meetings with the corporate counterparts for Tracy and Ken. Some GMs would be nervous about their people being in meetings with corporate without their presence.

In fact, we nicknamed one of the Matrix GMs, "Peter Paranoid." This guy is frightened of everything. He can find a problem if you give him a trash bag filled with twenty-dollar bills. We all wonder why Matrix puts up with him. In my opinion, and that of other GMs who know him, his behavior is motivated by the need to keep people from realizing how little he really knows about operating a hotel.

He will bury himself, his staff and corporate people with useless numbers and statistics, while his hotel continues to receive some of the lowest guest scores in the region. I would love to interview him using RCL just to find out what makes him behave the way he does. However, even if RCL points out the elements that influence his behavior, he will still be, as far as I am concerned, a little weasel who cannot earn the respect of his own staff. I believe this guy is one of those people who will make things better by simply going away. We all know that he has the protection of the VP of Finance, although no one

120

knows why. If the Finance VP left, Peter's remaining time at Matrix could be counted in minutes.

YOU SHOULD KNOW

Sometimes you have to give up and just terminate the problem. Recognizing when this is the right solution is sometimes difficult.

I look forward to driving with Ken and Tracy to corporate. I'm interested in what progress each of them has made by using RCL.

As they walk in and we head for my car, I notice a number of our people standing around the front desk. The personnel in my hotel always get excited when someone is going up to headquarters. They wish us well and tell us to be careful driving. These are good people who are excited, if not anxious, about our trip. Over the years, I've noticed this spontaneous occurrence repeatedly and have just as often wondered what makes them excited or anxious. I bet RCL could tell me. Maybe I'll find out later after I get good at putting the theory into practice. Right now, I am interested in how my first attempts, although being tested through others, are working out.

I start the car and begin chitchatting. Chitchat is a wonderful southern custom whereby no business is conducted until the participants first talk for a few minutes about family, friends, the weekend, whatever. I love the custom and think it adds a note of civility to all meetings. However difficult the impending matter, there is always time for chitchat and for creating, as a professor of mine might say, "communication capital." Funny how I remember his statement as if it were yesterday instead of back in my college days.

I initiate the discussion by asking Ken how his new house is coming. That elicits a five-minute rage directed at his contractor. It seems Ken sold his house and then found out that his new home would not be ready for another month. That means spending a month or more in the hotel with his wife and two dogs. Even though we're providing them large connecting rooms with a kitchen and living room, it's still a hotel and after a while any hotel, however accommodating, gets old.

When you add the fact that the staff knows he's living on property, it can make for never-ending work. We talk about making sure, when he goes up to his rooms, that the desk staff will call him only in those situations when they would have called him at home.

After venting, Ken starts to smile. "After all, it could be worse. I could have to pay for staying in the hotel."

I look surprised. "You're not?" We laugh and turn our attention to Tracy.

Ken asks Tracy about her trip to Washington over the weekend with her latest boyfriend. She tells us it was a great holiday. She stayed at the Royal Plaza on New Hampshire Avenue. The small suite was spectacular and the service impeccable, all for only fifteen hundred dollars a night.

We laugh about the ADR and talk about what services were provided. She says that when she picked up the phone, it only rang once and someone answered by saying, "How may I help you?" A few minutes after ordering breakfast, the phone rang with a request to deliver the food. When she said okay, there was an instant knock on the door—the waiter had called the room from the hallway. He brought in with breakfast *The Wall Street Journal*, *The New York Times*, and *USA Today*. The cable system had 230 channels that included such things as Sky News, the Saudi Network, eight movie channels, and all sports and network programming. She liked the experience but did not feel the need to go back, which I find interesting.

While I want to ask why she feels that way, I'm more interested in her and Ken's use of RCL. I ask her to tell me about the interviews she conducted.

"The process of talking to people about reward systems, confidence, and personal payoffs takes some time," she says. "The main problem is that I feel uncomfortable just sitting around talking and not getting anything done."

"How many of your people have you talked to?" I ask.

"Three of seven."

"How do you feel about the information you've gotten on the three?"

"It's good, but I'm not sure it's worth the time. Getting them to talk is like pulling teeth."

"Keep trying and let me know when you've finished all the interviews."

She hesitates. "Okay."

When Tracy says she will do something, she will. I'm not worried. She'll stick with it and get RCL on track and make it work. I have confidence in her.

KNOWING YOU

Knowing the difference between failing at a task and making another mistake is important.

Ken chimes in. "My experience is less positive than I thought it would be."

"What happened?" I ask him.

"My talk with Bob revealed nothing about his motivations, but it did make my job harder."

"Why do you think that?"

"I think Bob thought he was getting the promotion."

"Why would he think that?"

"Well, the relationship he has with you is one factor."

"What relationship?"

"You know, the joking around and kidding."

I laugh. "Oh, and he thought that would make up for his lack of education, training, and the experience necessary for the promotion?"

Ken replies, "People think crazy things when they don't understand how things really work. He never said that he deserved the job or even that he expected to get it, but I have the feeling he did."

"So what do you think will be the outcome?"

"I have no idea. I can't get him to talk and level with me. He's evasive. He acts like I'm going to fire him if he tells me the truth. I give up. I don't know what to do."

We drive in silence for a while, each of us thinking about our own particular problems.

My immediate problem is that I'm about to make a presentation about a motivation theory, and my first two attempts at using it seem to be producing less than stellar results. What to do?

I realize that once I decided RCL was a good idea, I just threw it at a couple of problems without the proper training and background. The concept is very good. My execution has been horrible.

I ask no one in particular, "What if, instead of just giving you an outline of what to do, we actually held a seminar to learn the proper way to implement RCL?"

"I would like that very much," Tracy says, "and could I stop doing interviews until I know more?"

"Ditto," Ken says.

"Yeah," I tell them. "Maybe I should go back to the drawing board on this one. It seemed like a good idea at the time, but I went too fast. I should have known nothing is that easy."

I have an uneasy feeling about this conversation. It's not my failures in trying to use RCL, though, that bothers me. It's something about Tracy and Ken. Is it something they said? Or is it something unspoken? Their reluctance, their attitudes, their lack of enthusiasm for RCL? Whatever it is, my intuition is picking it up loud and clear. It definitely is not a good signal.

Yes, something is nagging me and I don't know what. I hate it when that happens. I also know that my subconscious, preconscious, or whatever Spencer would call it, will work on it and yield results—and not when I am ready but when it is ready. So I let go of it for the time being.

We continue on our trip and I stop in Huntersville at a Shell station to take a break. Ken and I get coffee, and Tracy gets water.

I tell Ken and Tracy that I'm still going to present the ideas behind RCL but that I will add that we need a seminar, preferably from Dr. Spencer, about how best to implement the program. I wonder aloud if the VP will go for the expense involved in the education of our people. I have a guess as to what it might cost but am not really sure what Spencer would charge. They both agree it's a good approach and that if the VP buys the idea, she will surely buy the education part of the plan.

In a few minutes, I will be making the presentation. Within an hour, we will know one of two things: The VP will either say, "Thanks for thinking of us, but we will pass on this one," or she will say she "needs more information on the idea and the costs involved." If it's the latter, I have an extra book for her. If it's "thanks, but no thanks," I'll have to rethink my plan of going it alone. I really want to try the RCL approach.

KNOWING YOU

Do you have the courage to go it alone?

Matrix, whose full corporate name is Matrix Management Solutions, L.L.C., is housed in a three-story colonial office building. The corporation is a full service

125

hotel and country club management company that holds and manages properties in North Carolina, Tennessee, Virginia, and Georgia. In addition, it operates hotels for third party investors. Matrix manages two country clubs in North Carolina, one of which it also owns—a thousand acre, twenty-seven hole, gated community. They own and operate twenty-three hotels of their own and manage eight for other owners.

The employees own Matrix. Various staff and line people are placed on the board of directors in a systematic rotation. Matrix is very well known in the Southeast, and the longevity of its senior people is remarkable, particularly in the hospitality industry.

The corporate offices are furnished in a tasteful but comfortable manner. The landscaping is elegant and simple. Complementing the sense of stability is the feeling that personnel evidently can select their own furnishings. The result is a nice mixture of all styles that creates an environment of individuality.

The people at Matrix are hard working and dedicated to the idea that a good management company can make a difference. As a result, they try not to manage roadside properties or run member-owned country clubs.

Regarding the former, they believe that too many outside factors influence the occupancy of a roadside hotel for a management company to do more than control costs. As for the latter, member-owned country clubs are a nightmare of ever-changing board of governor members that results in changing the focus and direction of management based on the loudest voice on the board. People in the business know that new board members can mean "out with the old" management company and "in with the new." I bet RCL would work for country club management.

As we pull up to the visitor parking area, Ken says, "Good luck with your presentation."

Tracy adds, "I can't wait to hear what they say about your idea."

"Hey, guys," I reply, "It's not my idea. It's Spencer's concept that I think will help everyone who uses it properly, not like I just tried to do with you two."

"Maybe I did it wrong," says Tracy.

"No, you did all you could with the information you had," I tell her.

Ken says, "Maybe it doesn't work on everyone."

"I think it works for everyone who is interested in doing better. And the people who don't want to improve and change and get better need to move on," I respond.

"I love it when you get fired up like that," Tracy says with a smile as she punches me lightly on the shoulder.

KNOWING YOU

A good job can lead to a great career, and passion for what you do can lead to happiness.

As we get out of the car, I think, "Let's put some lipstick on this pig."

Martha, the receptionist, smiles as we walk into the foyer and says hello to all of us by name. She is a well-trained professional. She picks up the phone to call the vice president and asks if we would like to wait in the lounge. We tell her yes, walk behind her desk, and turn right. The lounge is directly off the boardroom, which is used for P & L meetings, presentations, and any meetings attended by more than four people; each executive office has a small meeting table that can seat four.

The boardroom is a high-tech wonder with electronically controlled whiteboards and state of the art audio/video capabilities. With a touch of a button, a presenter can call up flat screen monitors that rise out of the table at various locations. In addition, the room has the capability of connecting to the Internet or the corporate main frame computer for conference calls and long distance meetings.

The other GMs joke that you have to go to college just to work the table. But they, like me, love it and appreciate the fact that Matrix is not about to lose the race between retirement and obsolescence. I also think that the room itself portrays a sense of confidence in the future. A potential client will feel reassured that this company is here to stay.

As we walk to the lounge, the vice president of operations opens the door and walks out of the boardroom. She smiles and says hello to us and then turns to me and says, "Are we ready?" I answer yes and follow her up the stairs to her third floor office.

We reach her office and she puts the notebook she was carrying on her conference table. Her office is elegant and large, but not intimidating. The atmosphere is one of personal priorities and an attention to business. Her whiteboard is half-filled with locations and numbers; the other half is clean.

She puts everything away and sits down at the table with me. I know that from that moment until our allotted time is up, I will have her full attention. On one hand, I appreciate the focus; but on the other, I sometimes feel a little uncomfortable being in her spotlight. After some chitchat, she asks how things are going and we talk for a while about the hotel business in my area.

"What do the next three months look like in Charlotte?" she asks.

"Fair, but a little below last year."

"Have they gotten the Convention and Visitors Bureau off dead center?"

"They finally have a new director, but the damage has already been done," I tell her.

"We'll pay for that last guy's incompetence for the next three years."

"You're right. The whole town has been living off the past. We failed to notice that no one was working on the future."

"I understand that has changed now and that there is some accountability."

"There is and I can see the positive changes already."

"Good, we can use some help with those occupancy numbers. You wanted to meet to discuss this new motivation theory. Tell me about...what is it called? I have it in my notes. Oh, yes, Reality Check for Leaders. Why is it different from any other management theory?"

"Well the theory is very practical and is based on three essential pieces of information relating to an individual. Dr. Mark Spencer believes that current theories miss the mark when it comes to motivation."

She laughs. "That's interesting that he is arguing with his professor friends, but what is it and how could we use it here?"

"I believe if we apply this approach to our day-to-day management, we will be focusing on the most important element in leadership—motivation management. Reality Check for Leaders can help us understand how people, (1) decide how hard they will work, and (2) believe how well they will perform."

"Is this a long, drawn-out theory that will take consultants days and days of billable time to teach us?"

"No, although I would recommend we spend a day with Dr. Spencer to get up to speed."

"What will that cost?"

"I'm not sure. I wanted to wait for your reaction before I went any further."

"You really like this, don't you?" she says.

"Yes, I think it can really help us get a handle on performance and motivation."

"Have you tried it?"

"Yes, and to answer your next question, it did not work out as I had planned."

She laughs. "I like that candor. Even though it failed the first time or two, you want to go on?"

"RCL did not fail, I did. I tried to move too fast and only gave my people part of the theory. That's why it didn't work."

She looks at me, thinking, and just then her phone rings. She will, as everyone knows, ignore the ringing—three times and it stops. Martha, downstairs, knows the rule: three rings and take a message. It's a good payoff to know that her focus is on me and nothing else.

After my presentation she says, "Here is what I'm willing to do. If Spencer is not outrageously expensive, we can invite him here to meet with all of our GMs and company presidents. When we divide his cost up among the participants, it should be within the budgets of everyone. Why don't you get back to me with the cost and a schedule? Keep this to yourself until we know more about the numbers. Oh, and do you have an extra copy of his book you could leave with me?"

YOU SHOULD KNOW

Creative, challenging work is a personal payoff that all good leaders pursue.

I answer, "I do," and give her the book along with some information on the SISP that Spencer had mentioned.

"What's this SISP?" she asks.

"It's a profile Spencer recommended to us."

"Is it his?"

"No, but he likes the format and the information."

"Do you want me to complete this, too?"

"Well, I didn't want to push my luck, but yes, this could help, too."

"Okay. We can make a decision on all of this after you get the information we need."

"Great. I'll get back to you ASAP."

"Good. Are we done?"

As I get up, I say, "Yes, and thank you for hearing me out about RCL. I'm excited about the potential for our company."

We walk to the door and her assistant hands three messages to her and one to me. I read mine. "Oh, great," I say sarcastically.

"What?"

"The owner of the Hampton just came by and threw a hissy fit on the property again. This is a call from Stan the GM. He wants to know what to do."

"Let me know what happens with him and how you resolve it. Maybe you can use RCL on CF."

I laugh. "How did you know his nickname?"

She smiles. "That's why I make the big money."

I leave, smiling and feeling encouraged by the excellent payoff I've received: She took my advice.

CHAPTER TEN

MOTIVATING UP AND DOWN

While most of today's jobs do not require great intelligence, they do require greater frustration tolerance and personal discipline.

James P. Comer

I say goodbye to the VP. Tracy and Ken have not finished their meetings, so I go to the employee break room to get a cup of coffee. Cluster, the man who owns the Hampton Inn, is one of the biggest constraints my GM and I have to face. He inherited everything he owns and, from what I understand, he is a real loser when it comes to business judgment. I don't know him well and, if the truth were told, I do all I can to not have to deal with him. I often think that someone should write a self-help book called, *How to Spend as Little Time as Possible with People*

You Don't Like. Regardless of my personal preference, it's part of my job to deal with him.

I know from experience that any crisis he perceives can usually be solved without the stress and tension he brings to the situation. I also know that being the center of attention is very important to him. I wonder if RCL can help me in this situation. Everyone has to motivate up sometimes. Could I do a Reality Check on this guy? If so, it could help me understand him and how to deal more effectively with him.

I call Stan back to ask what Cluster's problem is this time. Stan tells me that Cluster wants to give twenty rooms away during Speed Week. Speed Week is one of two NASCAR four-day events held in Charlotte every year. People make room reservations months in advance. The race is one of the scheduled events that all hotels in the area count on to help meet revenue projections. The cost to the Hampton for meeting Cluster's demands would be around ten thousand dollars in revenue and another ten thousand dollars in additional expenses for relocating displaced guests—the Hampton would have to pay the difference between their ADR and that of the Diamond Creek Inn.

When Stan tried to explain the situation to him, Cluster went ballistic. He shouted profanities in the GM's office and generally acted like a lunatic. He was so loud that people in the lobby asked what was going on. Cluster shouted that this was his hotel and he would do whatever he pleased. He'd have their jobs if they didn't get him the room numbers right then. His tirade went on and on, every other word a profanity.

Stan is upset, but he laughs when I suggest that there are twenty six thousand words in the English language and this guy is stuck on nine of them. We talk a few more minutes and agree that we will walk twenty rooms to the Diamond. We hope that staying at the Diamond will help the displaced guests be more understanding. The last thing the Hampton needs is a decrease in our guest satisfaction scores.

Cluster is not only loud and crude but also cheap. I know that the guy bleeds the hotel for all it is worth. He constantly borrows money for projects that he describes as wonderful opportunities to increase revenues for the hotel. To my knowledge, in the five years that Matrix has managed the Hampton, not one dollar of a "loan" has been returned, let alone any profits.

As far as capital items for the Hampton are concerned, he always pushes for the cheapest possible alternative. For Waldo Cluster, nothing is ever too cheap to put in his Hampton. Moreover, anyone the Hampton deals with has to be the cheapest—contractors, landscapers, vendors, and any other service providers. "Cheapest" doesn't mean "least expensive," however. Cluster does not seem to understand the difference between inexpensive and cheap.

Stan and I have attended a number of capital meetings at his office. The results are always the same. The first time I met him he actually said, "No one told me the furniture would wear out so fast." I tried to explain that (1) the furniture we had to replace was not very well made, and (2) we had increased occupancy. Therefore, wear and tear was more pronounced. Seemingly, both facts went over his head and he proceeded to rant about the cost associated with meeting the standards of that bunch of idiots in Memphis. He went on and on about "all the things that the franchise holder has done" to him, as if the franchise holder even knows who he is. The guy is not just slow; he is paranoid.

As Waldo drones on at these meetings, his assistant just nods his head at whatever the runt says. I don't know what the assistant does other than fetch coffee, pens, and paper for Cluster to use. Cluster's bookkeeper is a lady who is probably no more than thirty years old but looks fifty. One has to wonder what the IRS would think of all the "loans" the little guy has made to himself. That capital meeting ended, as they all do, with his picking the cheapest alternative and walking out of the room without one word of thanks.

When Stan and I finish talking, we determine that this temper tantrum of Cluster's will cost the hotel almost a thousand dollars per friend multiplied by twenty friends.

The demoralizing aspect of the situation is that Stan and I both know that at year-end review, the decrease in revenues and department profit will be brought up by Cluster. Then he will lie and say, "Well, no one told me how much it would cost."

Before I hang up, Stan thanks me for listening to his rants about the owner. I tell him that I understand his frustration and will get back to him with some ideas on how to deal with the guy.

Drinking more coffee, I start thinking about what to do. Is there a way that I could motivate up using RCL? Just then, Tracy walks in. She sits down with her bottled water and asks, "How did it go?"

"Well, she wants more information on costs and scheduling. How did your meeting go?"

"There are plans for a regional Concentrated Call Program. The idea is to use sales teams from the five hotels in the region and cross-sell each property. The teams will go to Atlanta and cover areas prescreened for each hotel."

Just as she finishes, Ken enters the room and says, "I'm ready to go, if you guys are." We head for the car and the ninety-minute drive back to the Diamond.

My presentation to the VP went well. I should feel good, but something still is nagging at me. It's the way Tracy and Ken were responding to RCL earlier, but I can't put my finger on it yet. I always get impatient waiting for my brain to work through something like this. Oh, well, a flash of brilliance will strike me eventually, I hope.

As we merge onto the interstate, Ken tells us about his meeting with his front office counterpart. The purpose of the meeting was to review the front desk situation at the Diamond.

Matrix has a policy of "re-explaining" the objectives of any particular job after a ninety-day review is conducted by the GM. I submitted Ken's evaluation about two weeks ago. Bill Johnson, the man responsible for all front desk operations at the corporate level, wanted to review the objectives assigned to our front desk managers. Before discovering RCL, I thought that the process of redefining objectives was a good idea. However, I now know that some of the RCL elements are missing from the plan of motivating front desk managers to perform at specific levels. We do a great job in defining the tasks that have to be performed, but we miss on the interest factor. Interest level is the key to real motivation, and we don't really approach the subject with our people. Additionally, understanding personal payoffs is not our strong suit.

As Ken and Tracy continue to talk about their experiences, I think about how much more substance RCL is going to add to my understanding of people and the way they operate at work.

Around four thirty on most weekdays, the city of Charlotte begins to empty out. The traffic begins to build in all directions out of the city. From five thirty to six thirty, the interstate highways become stop-and-roll parking lots. While there has been an explosion of construction of city-condos, the beautiful environment of the surrounding areas outside the inner city draws thousands of commuters. As a result, getting into the city at this time of day is no problem, but getting out is another thing. I drive all the way to our hotel exit on cruise control, while north-bound traffic is backed up for miles. We pull into the parking lot at about 5:30 p.m. and head to our offices. I have a few phone messages about past due invoices and five emails that can wait.

I walk the property and talk to the people who work the three to eleven shift. These people have a different set of payoffs from those on other shifts. Working from three in the afternoon to eleven at night is certainly not ideal for families with children or single people with social lives, yet we have a stable crew in the restaurant, lounge, and banquet area every night.

I find it interesting that there are both men and women who choose to work during this time period. An obvious financial payoff is the higher tips in the restaurant and lounge. However, that can't explain all the people who work for just the base salary. I understand that sometimes that is the only position available and people at the entry level will work those hours just to get started in the business. However what about the people who choose three to eleven? What do they like about those hours? I've never asked. I bet that learning that answer will lead to other discoveries about their payoffs.

Everything is in order, so I leave the hotel and head to my health club to get in some aerobic work. Before the day is over, maybe I can spend some time with some of my other problems.

The drive is pleasant, and I decide not to think about work. I just want to relax and let my mind be free of all the stuff that usually crowds it. It feels so good that I vow to do this more often.

Then, suddenly, the gnawing feeling that I had twice earlier today about Tracy and Ken is back. I pick up my cell phone, press the contacts button, scroll to Dr. Spencer's number, and punch "Send."

Then I laugh out loud. There is no way he will answer. I bet he screens all of his calls, or more likely, never answers and just listens to his messages. Wrong!

"This is Mark Spencer." At first, I think it's a recording. By the time I realize he has answered, he is saying, "Can you hear me?"

I'm laughing. "Dr. Spencer, I can hear you. This is John B..."

He interrupts, "I already know who you are. Modern technology."

"How are you?"

"Fine. What's going on?"

"I have a problem."

"Of course, why else would you call?"

This man can be intimidating. I clear my throat, trying to calm down. "I have two of my managers using RCL, and it's not going so well."

"Let me see if I understand. You have them using RCL, but you're not using it yourself. Is that what you just told me?"

Laughing, I say, "I hate it when you do that."

"And, soon, they will be more skilled at using it than you. Is that what you want?"

"Well, no."

"I assume you will fix that immediately."

"Yes, I will."

"Good. Let's talk about your two managers. Here's what happened. They perceive they have the skills to do something new, such as use RCL. Quickly they discover they are wrong. They struggle, and self-perceived skill problems develop. Then they start thinking, 'This isn't worth the effort.' Translated this means, 'The pain and effort this is causing me aren't worth the payoffs I was hoping to get.' Now they have two problems: a payoffs problem and a perceived skills problem. The end result always is the same: Their motivation sags. So they procrastinate, drag their feet, and make excuses. Is that what you're seeing, John?"

"Yes, exactly. And I've been blaming them for not showing as much interest in RCL as I wanted them to, rather than placing the blame on myself where it belongs."

"Look, John, just listen to what they say. They will tell you what's wrong. They're asking for help and you're not hearing them."

"Bingo. That's what's been nagging me all day, some things they said. I got it—now."

"One more thing, what is their standard pattern of behavior, their style, if you will?"

"Their what?"

"Their behavior as it relates to work. I will send you information about how to determine it other than by observation."

"Thank you, Dr. Spencer. So what is this 'behavior style' you're talking about?"

"Look, I don't have time to explain it now. Send me an email and I'll reply with the information you need."

"Yes, sir, I will."

"John, this is important. Do it. Okay, I have to go. Bye."

"Thank you, Dr. Sp...." He is already gone.

I was still driving when I called Spencer. Now I am in my usual parking space at the club, not even remembering how I got here. I need to have a good workout and give my mind a rest before I can process all of this.

The club is packed by the time I get there. It is six thirty and all of the cardio machines are filled. I do not want to lift weights. After a few minutes of talking to some of the trainers I know and generally standing around, I decide to pass on a workout. I leave the club and go to a nearby Subway to get a tuna sandwich and some chips.

When I get there, the young girl behind the counter is angry and vocal. After taking my order, she ignores me and continues telling the other high school-aged workers how unfair the boss has been. I can hear every word she is saying, and as I approach the cash register, she says to me without looking up, "$5.85," and then continues to complain to her co-workers.

'Finally, I just can't stand it anymore. I say, in a voice loud enough for all to hear, "Young lady, if you hate your job and your boss so much, then quit because I, for one, am tired of hearing you whine. Now give me my change and be quiet."

With that, the adults in the store start applauding, and she drops my change on the counter and stalks off.

A young man comes up and says, "I'm sorry. She does that all the time."

"No need for you to apologize," I tell him.

He hands me my change and I leave, wondering if there are times when you have to say, "Forget RCL. This simply is wrong and it has to stop." I have always been a believer in cutting your losses. RCL can help in many situations that need more information before a decision can be made, but sometimes the facts are staring you in the face. You just have to acknowledge them and take the necessary steps to correct the obvious problem.

By the time I get to my car, I have calmed down some. My conclusion is that RCL cannot explain what was happening with the young girl inside the Subway, but maybe I am being too hasty. Okay, if RCL were applied to this situation, what would you get? First, it is not a case of the young girl having a misperception about her job skills, not in that job. In other words, it is not a confidence problem. What about the payoffs she is pursuing? Obviously, she is unhappy. That's it. She is not getting the payoffs she desires, whatever they are. So, it is a payoffs problem.

Now, what is the third element in RCL? It takes me a minute to remember: Rewarded behaviors get repeated. What was it the young man said? She does this all the time. Okay, then her behavior is being rewarded, but how? Well, she certainly gets a lot of attention. In addition, showing anger, speaking your mind, and telling people what you think can be rewarding. Furthermore, behaving inappropriately can be viewed as a way to get back at the boss. Overall, I would say she is being rewarded for her bad behavior. Moreover, since rewarded behavior is repeated, more bad behavior can be expected.

Then I realize that this is exactly what is happening with the Hampton owner. He behaves inappropriately, he gets rewarded for it (in his own way), and he continues abusing the staff at the Hampton or anyone who will let him. That makes perfect sense. Thanks, RCL.

Driving home, I try to build a personality profile in my mind of the owner of the Hampton. I know he inherited all of the money he has, and word has it that he lost a considerable amount of it to con men who offered him get-rich-quick schemes. He isn't married and spends most of his time trying to look good and be respected. Whenever I ask about him at the corporate office, the only response I get is that he is one of the more difficult clients they have. It seems the approach at Matrix is the less said about him, the better. They have also adopted my strategy of spending as little time as possible with him. That will no longer work for me, given my offer to help Stan deal with him. Knowing more about his payoffs will help me in contending with him. Using RCL, I begin to outline in my mind what I know about the man.

The first element of RCL is this: Perceived skills and interests determine motivation. When people perceive their skills to be strong, they tend to push for results. On the other hand, when they think their skills are inadequate, they hold back, procrastinate, and fail to do what is necessary to get results.

My guess is that this is a problem for the Hampton owner. He is not very skilled at leadership or at anything else. I need only look at the people with whom he chooses to surround himself to immediately understand that he likes having them around so that he can blame them for his mistakes. He makes sure that they know they work *for* him and not *with* him. This is obvious because, even after years of working for him, they still have to call him "Mr. Cluster."

When it comes to the next element of RCL—rewarded behaviors arc rcpcated—I am not sure either. On one hand, he uses his erratic and insensitive behavior to manipulate people to respond to him the way he wants. Everyone who works for him seems to say, "How high do you want me to jump?" I know he likes this. So, on this count, he surely is rewarded for his behavior. That's why he repeats it. He yells and screams, and everybody jumps to meet his demands.

Okay, we are our own worst enemy. We have created a little Hitler in the way we all respond to him.

However, when I look at this element (rewarded behaviors are repeated) on a larger scale with him, I get confused. He keeps losing money on one business venture after another. That is, he is seldom, if ever, rewarded. Yet he continues investing in new ventures. He is repeating behaviors that are not rewarded. How do you explain that? A shrink would call that insanity.

First, he has abundant evidence that he does not have the skills necessary to be a successful entrepreneur. Second, he does not stack up favorably to his successful father. Surely, he knows this. He has lost too much money not to recognize his lack of ability. Yet he still keeps trying. Maybe that's because he has very pronounced feelings of inadequacy and he keeps trying to make money to overcome his poor self-esteem. That is a good bet.

In addition, he probably will continue until he loses all of his inherited money and everyone else's. When you feel inadequate, you are in pain; so you fight, scratch, and claw trying to find your way out of it. While it makes sense that rewarded behavior is repeated, I also can see how behaviors that are not rewarded might be repeated, at least for a while.

I pull into the driveway of my home and press the remote for the garage door. When I walk into the house, it seems cold and a little damp. I flip the master switch and instantly the whole place becomes brighter. I dislike overhead lights and have my home wired so that floor and table lamps turn on with one or two switches. Each room is in turn wired to do the same thing. All the lights have dimmer switches, and I can set everything in ten seconds. I put the tuna sandwich in the kitchen, turn up the heat, and go to change into a warm sweater, a lined pair of sports slacks, and some thick socks.

I walk to my favorite room in the house—one that my wife and I named "the quiet room"—and take about ten minutes to light a fire. There is something about a real fire that brings a pure comfort payoff beyond the obvious warmth.

The room is twenty feet by twenty-five feet with glass and mahogany bookcases. One wall contains a sixty-inch plasma television and music system and a computer/photography area. It and the rest of the room are lined with two-inch thick glass bookshelves. There are nine lamps in the room—seven come on with a wall switch and two turn on with timers. I have a big, comfortable—if not attractive—leather chair surrounded by tables and lamps.

My current reading material is sitting on the table nearest my chair. I like to read two or three books at a time. My reading in this room is always for pleasure, and I enjoy fiction the most. I keep my nonfiction and professional books in my study; however, RCL has become so fascinating that it is one of the few work-related books that make it to this room.

I turn on the television to Fox news and watch my favorite news show of the day. *The Fox News Hour* with Brit Hume is on from six o'clock to seven o'clock and provides me with almost all of the news I can handle in a day. In the morning, I hear the rest of the story from the local National Public Radio station. With those two sources, I am comfortable that I can remain up to date on current affairs.

I get my sandwich, chips, and a Diet Pepsi and sit down to watch the news and eat. By 7:00 p.m., I have finished my dinner, relaxed a bit, and caught up on the news. I'm ready to get back to RCL and our Hampton Inn owner.

I head for my study to work on the problem. I sit down and start to write. One, deep down, he perceives his skills to be inadequate; and as a result, he has serious confidence problems. Two, he gets rewarded for his obnoxious behavior around people, but the rewards definitely do not derive from financial profitability or growth of his business ventures.

The next question is, What about personal payoffs? What could they be? What does he work for in his life? Why does he work at all? Given his failure rate in business, what keeps him going year after year? I try to think about how he behaves as a way of understanding his payoffs. If past behavior is the best predictor of future behavior, past behavior also offers some clues as to what motivates individuals to behave the way they do. Although Dr. Spencer has stated that the best way to find out about people's payoffs is to ask, I know I have no chance of getting close enough to Cluster to ask, nor do I want to.

Besides, RCL should work for motivating up as well as down. Okay, what payoffs does he have? First, anyone with that kind of business track record who keeps on throwing money away is trying to prove a point. Is he trying to prove something to his father or to himself? So, one payoff is proving he is good at business. I don't know him well enough to know about his family or friends, but I can predict that for him the illusion of "doing business" is important.

Second, taking one look at his staff reveals an overwhelming need for approval, regardless of the source. The people around him are a sad group of small-minded, frightened individuals. In meeting after meeting, I notice that they never disagree with him. After meetings and in the hallways of his offices after he has gone, they make fun of him. They ridicule almost every mistake he makes. He accepts their compliments without regard for their real opinions of him. Approval is a big payoff for him.

Third, the need for attention could be another payoff. I have heard about his outrageous behavior too many times not to believe that part of his behavior can be explained by one of the basic principles in Psychology 101, a cry for attention. I think that getting attention is yet another payoff.

Fourth, improving his self-image likely is a payoff, as I mentioned earlier. I've noticed in the few times I've spent with him that he treats everyone with disdain. I want to confirm with Stan my impression that Cluster never actually says goodbye or thank you to him, that he is always late for meetings, that he keeps people waiting while he answers his cell phone, and on and on. Again, if I remember my basic psychology, these are ways people try to feel better about who they are, to feel worthy.

How many payoffs do you need to see in someone before you can understand why he behaves the way he does? These four payoffs certainly paint a sad picture, but are they accurate? I have no real expertise in psychology. Do you have to be a Ph.D. like Spencer to understand a person? No. Otherwise, RCL would not be of much use. I'm going with this as a test of the theory. If it can't work in all situations and interactions, it won't be of help to most people. It's with the difficult leadership problems that most of us need help.

Tomorrow I plan to set up an appointment to see Cluster. Motivating him to stop acting like a jerk will be a big accomplishment and a very good payoff for me. I wonder if I can really do that. My lack of confidence is showing. And, for now, that's okay.

I finish writing and head for the quiet room. It is almost nine. I check to see if there are any good, old movies on TCM. I find that most of the time, old movies tell good stories without the need to preach. There are the good guys and the bad guys, and the good guys win most of the time. Right now, nothing special is on, so I read for an hour or so and go to bed. I have a busy day tomorrow, and I fall asleep thinking about how best to tackle the Waldo Cluster problem.

CHAPTER ELEVEN

THIS IS REALITY CHECK

In order to feel good about himself, a child must be successful in his own eyes, not just in your eyes. Self-esteem is an inner feeling: Sometimes it corresponds with outer reality, and sometimes it doesn't.

Stanley I. Greenspan

My morning starts with a smile on my face when I notice a light dusting of snow on the ground. The snow is falling gently; the headlights of my car pick up the flakes and make it seem like a real storm. But I expect it will be another one of those "Hollywood" snowfalls—the snow is on the lawns, trees, and shrubbery but not on the streets.

As I drive to the hotel, I hear on the radio that the high for today will be forty-nine degrees, which means it will all be gone by noon. Tony C, my friend who lives in Buffalo, will rant about not seeing the ground for months on end, while I play as if it is really snowing. That's a good laugh for both of us.

The parking lot is almost dry when I get to the hotel, and the snow on the lawns and trees makes the property look like a postcard. I say good morning to the night crew and go to the kitchen to get a cup of coffee. The morning shift is already there getting the buffet ready for breakfast. With coffee in hand, I head to my office to get a jump start on the day.

It's too early to return phone calls but not too early to answer emails. I like the idea of people arriving at their jobs in the morning and finding my emails waiting for them. I'm convinced that if you keep in touch with people, they will be reasonable about any problems you might have. I answer the emails and start to compose one to Dr. Spencer.

He chastised me good about throwing Tracy and Ken into the fire of RCL without preparing them for it and for not using it to diagnose their own motivation problems using RCL. I put that out of my mind last night and gave Cluster's outrageous behavior the spotlight. That's just another example of how much impact he has on people and the negative way he affects productivity.

Back to Tracy and Ken. Spencer said Tracy had both confidence and payoffs problems when it came to implementing RCL. What I need to do is have a talk with her and remind her how smart and competent she is and help her see the payoffs at the end of the line if she will just work hard and use RCL effectively.

Spencer said Ken has the same two problems. He is less experienced than Tracy, so maybe I need to coach him some on how to handle the problem with his front desk person, Bob. I'll be able to show him the benefits and he will see the personal payoffs. That's simple enough.

Then I hear Dr. Spencer's voice saying, "Just listen to them. They will tell you what's wrong." That was on the phone call yesterday. I heard him say another time, "If you want to know, ask." He stressed that when people have problems, they usually know a solution that will work for them. "All you have to do is ask," he said.

And look at me. Look at what I'm doing. I'm trying to solve Tracy's and Ken's problems my own way without consulting with them. Old habits are hard to break. My way for years has been the same: I see a problem and I fix it. But that is not the RCL way.

Spencer also said, "Leaders believe they are supposed to solve all of the problems. How foolish can anyone be? Leaders do not have time. They are responsible for getting all problems solved, not for solving them all themselves." There's a big difference.

Okay, so I need to talk to Tracy and Ken and ask them what they think. They're dragging their feet on using RCL. I need to do a Reality Check on them: What's the problem? What's causing it? How do you, Tracy and Ken, want to solve it?

Maybe I'm finally getting into the swing of things. I'll check with them and see how soon we can get together. I'm ready.

I wonder if they are; they probably aren't. I'll figure out some way to get them ready. In the meantime, I guess I should wait. We can have a better discussion after they learn more about RCL.

I feel good. Any time I learn something new and make a good decision around it, I always feel inspired, more motivated, and more confident. RCL is doing so much for me. Now, if I can just help others see the personal payoffs in it for them.

Back to the email to Spencer. When I get my thoughts together, I am as brief as I can be. Spencer will appreciate that.

Dear Dr. Spencer:

Thank you for taking my call yesterday and giving me some good, sound advice. I intend to follow it. Please send information on behavior style and I will follow through with that as well.

I presented my thoughts about RCL to my boss, Ms. Long, the VP of Operations for Matrix Management Solutions. She requested that I ask you for information regarding a seminar for all of the Matrix GMs. She would like to know the amount of time and the cost associated with the seminar. I look forward to your response.

Have a good day.

John Battaglia
General Manager, Diamond Creek Inn

The auto response from Spencer says that he is out of the office but will be checking his emails at night.

I review my stock portfolio and the weather. The Dow is slowly moving upward. The weather forecast calls for cold nights and clear skies. By seven thirty, I have finished with the emails and memos from my department heads. I've responded to housekeeping regarding their need for additional linen, to a memo from Tracy asking about funds for a special Christmas promotion for our regular corporate people, and to my F & B Director about a salary increase for his assistant.

I have a great group of people. Do I convey to them how valuable they are to this operation? We get so busy around here that I can go days without mentioning what a great job they're doing. However, a "thank you" goes only so far. I need to know what their personal payoffs are. Why can't I start that today?

This reminds me that I have to talk to my F & B Director. I wonder again if Dr. Spencer's example in the D.C. seminar is really my restaurant manager. Knowing that information will help me say the right things in the staff meeting tomorrow.

I'm beginning to feel as if I'm on a roll. Nothing really has been accomplished yet, but I'm starting to see things more clearly. The picture is coming into focus. The problems are surfacing, and the pathway for getting them solved is opening up before my eyes. I say "getting them solved" rather than "solving them myself"—yes, I am definitely making progress. With that thought, I go looking for people on whom I can practice.

As I move around the hotel, I realize something very important about using RCL: It can't be done half-heartedly. If RCL is to work, both manager and employee have to believe that the information is important, important enough to take the time to sit down away from the normal day-to-day activities and talk. The manager must focus on the employee and the responses given.

I have a sudden thought that changes my approach. Instead of trying to talk to my people while they're working, I decide that I will present RCL at a staff meeting and then talk to each person one on one. The idea of a staff meeting where I present the basic concepts of RCL to my managers makes great sense. It will provide them with an understanding of why I will be asking questions about their payoffs and the other elements of RCL, while also giving me a good reason to go back to the book. Knowing something and knowing it well enough to teach it are two different levels of understanding, with the latter being the most valuable, by far.

I go back to my office and prepare a memo about tomorrow's staff meeting. The meeting will be in two parts and will start at 10:00 a.m. instead of 2:00 p.m. Part One will be a presentation of RCL by me, and Part Two will be the regular weekly staff meeting. I'm not interested in waiting all day to present the information; too many things can interfere with my goal of getting people to understand RCL.

By nine o'clock, I have made copies of the memo and distributed them. From nine to noon, I work on my presentation. After lunch, I put all my RCL material in a folder and slip it into my briefcase to take home. For the rest of the day, I do all of the things that any other GM does: put out some fires, deal with upset vendors, authorize some payments, and review occupancy figures. Of course, I think about my presentation for tomorrow, too.

I head home, fix dinner, and watch the news. However, the presentation keeps coming to mind. If I can convey the importance of RCL to my people tomorrow, my future leadership life will be much more productive.

The next morning I get to work around five thirty. I am always anxious about any presentation, and being in the office helps me relax. I drink coffee and go over my notes. I check the daily report and walk to the room that we use for our meetings. Although I have been in this room numerous times, it feels good to just stand here for a moment and get the feel of it.

I walk to the kitchen and say hello to the breakfast crew. Veterans all, they are happy and generally in a good mood. The housekeeping department is quiet this early, but Helen, the executive housekeeper, is in her office scheduling her people. She looks up as I walk in. We exchange a few words, and then I leave so I don't interrupt her train of thought. Proper scheduling can make a difference in departmental profit.

As the sun comes up, I walk the property. The air is crisp and cold. A slight wind feels good as I check the parking lot and landscaping.

I look up and see a number of room drapes opening and lights coming on. The Diamond is waking up. In another hour, the lobby and restaurants will be bustling with guests.

I approach the front double doors, and as they open, I see Rosie, the bell captain, taking the day's first group of USAirways pilots to the airport. We exchange good mornings, and I help him load the luggage into his van.

I hand him a twenty and ask him to take my car to be washed. The car wash takes about ten minutes and costs ten dollars. Rosie always offers the change, and I always refuse. We've been doing this for years, yet Rosie never takes his tip for granted. I've told him numerous times not to bother, but to no avail. First chance I get I'll ask him why he tries to return the change every time. And I'm going to do a Reality Check on him, too. Maybe I'll learn something helpful about him and RCL.

I go back to my office, work until around nine forty-five, and then head to the meeting. This presentation is going to be fun, but I feel nervous.

I walk into the staff meeting room and find about half of the people there. I say hello to everyone and get a cup of coffee. Stan, the GM at the Hampton, walks in and I introduce him to two people he hasn't yet met. As the room fills and ten o'clock approaches, I walk to the front of the table and start looking at my notes. People get coffee and juice and settle in to hear what I have to say.

"Good morning. I want to talk today about an approach to motivating people to perform at their best. But before I get started with telling you about Reality Check for Leaders, I want to emphasize what RCL is not." I write on the whiteboard and then comment briefly on each item:

What RCL Is NOT

1. Additional work you will have to do relative to leading your people.
2. A touchy-feely, my-intentions-were-good answer to the goals and objectives we all face.
3. A substitute for achievement.
4. 100% guaranteed to motivate everyone you try it on.
5. A graduate course in psychology.

I'm getting that great feeling that occurs when you know you're going to do well. Now that's a big payoff for me (although, as I write on the whiteboard, I realize this really needs to be a PowerPoint presentation).

What RCL IS

1. A technique for understanding why people behave the way they do.
2. Comprised of three fundamental elements.
3. Able to influence the difference between expected and real behavior.

I want to emphasize this, so I write on the board and quickly explain this diagram:

```
┌─────────────────────────────┐
│   Reality Check for Leaders  │
└─────────────────────────────┘
```

Expected Behavior   Real Behavior
       Norms   Acts

1. Everyone Has Self-perceived Skills and Interests
2. Rewarded Behavior Is Repeated
3. People Pursue Personal Payoffs

"Here is how RCL works. People think about how they are expected to think, feel, and behave. These expectations are called 'norms.' People view these norms through the filters of the three variables, or elements, I have listed here. These elements, therefore, determine how people will *actually* think, feel, and behave. The resulting thoughts, feelings, and behaviors are called 'acts.' Let's take a look at these three elements.

"First, self-perceived interest and skill levels. This is the question people ask themselves: 'Do I have the skills to do this job or even just this one task, and more important, do I have an interest in doing this task?'"

I turn to my people and say, "And remember this: It is not *your* opinion but the opinion of the person doing the job that counts. Do they believe they are able to perform the assigned tasks? Do they think they have the necessary interest in actually performing the task? Until their answer to both is yes, they will avoid the assignment for as long as possible."

I notice that both Tracy and Ken look a little uncomfortable with this discussion about self-confidence. I give each of them a reassuring smile. There is no doubt in my mind that they will overcome whatever doubt they have and soon will be using RCL to the benefit of everyone in their departments.

"Second, rewarded behavior is repeated. The question here is this: 'If I perform the assigned task successfully, will I be rewarded?' People who work on a sales commission basis and entrepreneurs clearly know their work behavior is rewarded. They know that their rewards are a function of their performance. They also know that there is no limit to what they can accomplish.

"Others, however, must rely on the organization's reward system. Assuming they can perform the task successfully, they then have to wait for an evaluation from someone else to determine if they have actually accomplished the goal and then have to wait for whatever rewards that may follow. If, in the individual's mind, the reward system is flawed, the willingness to perform is diminished. On the other hand, when the reward system is perceived as reliable, this contributes to the motivation to perform. In other words, rewarded behavior is repeated.

"This is the reason so much bad behavior is repeated. When people are rewarded for performing poorly, they continue to perform poorly. This happens in many companies where people are given across-the-board pay raises rather than raises based on performance.

"When people perform poorly and get pay raises, they continue performing poorly. Behavior that is rewarded is repeated, no matter whether it is good behavior or bad behavior. Behavior that is not rewarded is not repeated, at least not for very long."

I notice that Dean, my F & B director, has not made eye contact with me since I started this part of the discussion, so I pause until he looks up. I hold eye contact with him as I speak.

"If any of you are rewarding poor performance or are simply ignoring it, nothing will change. Rewarded behavior is repeated." He does not look away. I'm certain his restaurant manager is a problem. Now Dean knows that I know. It will be interesting to see what he does about it.

"Third, people pursue personal payoffs. If you understand the concept that people pursue personal payoffs, or 4P, you are able to appreciate the fact that we are all motivated by our own payoffs. Moreover, the payoffs are as different as people are different. The range of payoffs can go from the good feeling you get by helping others, to revenge. Payoffs can be positive or negative for society.

"While the concept of 4P initially seems elusive, the answers are reasonably easy to obtain. Believe it or not, finding out what an individual's payoffs are may be as easy as asking. If you want to know, ask. One of the reasons this relatively simple technique is overlooked most of the time is that we think the payoffs that motivate us are universal. Why should we ask? We already know, or so we think—a very big mistake for a leader to make."

As I wrap up the brief discussion on payoffs, I cannot help but think of Rosie. He appears to have a handle on the payoffs he wants. I'm going to do a Reality Check on him the next time he is free to talk.

"There you have the three elements that explain the difference between norms and acts, between what people are expected to do and what they actually do, between expected behavior and real behavior. There you have it." I turn and point to the whiteboard that has the outline of RCL.

"What I propose to do is sit down with each of you to listen to your thoughts about these three elements. You know that you all are special to me. The fact is, if you weren't doing a great job, you wouldn't be hearing this presentation." There is some nervous laughter. "I think RCL can be useful to you if you want to improve your leadership skills. Notice I said, 'if you want to.' The important point is that, although I have a continuing interest in leadership, some of you may not be so inclined. And, with RCL, if you're doing well in meeting your leadership goals and feel as if you do not want to alter your style, then there is no problem. Remember, it's your call.

"Finally, before I ask for questions, I want to try to paraphrase what Dr. Spencer says about RCL. Every year, leaders in all occupations continue to search for the best way to get things done with people. Moreover, almost every year the new approach that was considered the end-all, be-all solution becomes old news. He thinks the question should not be *how* do I motivate people but rather *what* makes people behave the way they do? Once you have those answers, you're on your way to becoming a more

157

effective leader. What I like about his comments is that his theory provides a method for really understanding behavior."

"If you choose not to employ this technique with your subordinates, you should at least use it to understand yourself better. I hope that our one-on-one sessions will help you with that. Let's take a break, get some coffee, and come back for questions. We have our regular meeting after this, so I won't take up much more of your time."

Before anyone can move, Vance stands up and says, "I have a lot of stuff to do if you want your hotel to stay open. Can I go?"

I say, "Can't win 'em all." People laugh. Vance leaves.

As he walks out the door, I tell him, "Vance, we're going to talk about you when you leave."

"I don't care," he says and keeps walking. I know he'll ask Helen about what was said, and I smile. One of the most unproductive things a person can do is to wish that someone's behavior will change.

After people have been milling around for a few minutes, I say, "Okay, let's see if there are any questions."

As the group sits down, Nicky, our catering manager, asks, "Will RCL work at home, too?" This draws a few laughs.

"Absolutely," I answer. "RCL provides you with a way of understanding anyone's behavior."

Nicky continues, "My son, who is fourteen, is driving me nuts." The people in the group who have no children laugh the loudest. Those with older children laugh and nod their heads knowingly. Those with teenagers laugh as they squirm in their seats.

"Seems like you're not alone when it comes to teenage problems," I respond. That gets a big laugh. "You can find out more about what he thinks if you have the patience. For sure, the attention can't hurt, and the worst thing that can happen is that there will be a few minutes of uncomfortable silence."

"I think I'll look this over and give it a try," she says.

"Wonderful, let us know how that works out. Now are there any other questions?"

"I have one," says Tracy. "But I don't want to mention names."

"If it's the same concern you had last week, we can talk about it after we conduct an RC on you."

Tracy looks puzzled and asks, "RC?"

"Yes, Reality Check. Any other questions?"

Stan says, "Last week you mentioned to me a way of finding out about people's interests and skills. Does Reality Check help with that?"

"Actually, it does. Dr. Spencer told us in the seminar I attended that the most non-threatening way to find out about a person's perceived skills and interests is to have them take the SISP. It's a profile that takes about forty minutes to complete and offers some great personal insights into how a person compares to others in our industry relative to individual skills and interests."

I want to tell them about the concept that we all create our own worlds and then behave rationally in those worlds, but time is short and we have to finish. I can tell them more about it when they take the profile in a week or so.

"Does anyone else have a question or a reaction to Reality Check for Leaders? We already know Vance's opinion." Everyone laughs.

Then the room turns quiet. I'm not sure if it's the normal I-don't-want-to-look-stupid problem or if the presentation did not go over well. I get my answer when I say, "Well, that's it then," and people start to applaud. The one thing I know from experience is that my people let me know with their silence when they do not appreciate a presentation or program.

159

"Who wants to run the staff meeting today?" I ask. "I have already talked enough for today."

Ken says he would like to try if no one minds. A number of people say, "Go for it," and he stands up.

As Helen helps him get started with our standard agenda, I'm still thinking about the presentation. They like this idea. I wonder how many will actually try RCL. It's hard to tell because often what happens is that people attend a seminar or presentation and walk out believing that the ideas they heard were the greatest thing since sliced bread. However, when they get back to their organizations, the existing reward system takes over and they soon lose interest in trying a new approach. Reality Check for Leaders has no chance of succeeding if the atmosphere in the organization is hostile to new approaches. I will make sure my people each have a chance to at least try RCL. It will be up to them to pursue the opportunity. What if...

My thoughts are suddenly interrupted by laughter and I look up. It seems they have caught me thinking about RCL instead of listening to occupancy reports. Tracy evidently scolded me for not paying attention, and I've been caught just as I've caught most of them before. There are a few more comments. We all have a good laugh and then get down to the numbers. It's a good thing we've worked together long enough for them to understand that I'm not discounting them.

Occupancy is up about seven percent, with most of the gains coming from the Sales Department. Tracy gets a round of applause and makes it a point to thank her sales people. Housekeeping is over budget in the laundry room, even considering the increased occupancy. While the overtime is understandable, the total per room cleaning cost has increased. Each department in turn presents weekly summaries of expenses and revenues.

Ken presents the likely business for next week, and Banquets outlines up and coming functions. The meeting ends around eleven o'clock, and people head for their various places around the hotel.

I did well. Or at least that is what I choose to think. From what I know about public speaking, head nods seem important as a measure of understanding. Either my people understood and appreciated RCL or they were playing me. Unfortunately, I have experienced their lack of interest and enthusiasm about other concepts and new ideas; then, it was obvious through their words and actions that some of the ideas I had presented did not fly.

While I erase the whiteboard and pick up my notes, I take the opportunity to think about how the presentation could have been better. The more I think about RCL, the more excited I become. Maybe there's a future for me in conveying this concept to other people? I sure like teaching.

Do I like it more than being a general manager? This is challenging and fun; however, I do love my leadership role. I start looking forward to my first non-employee audience. Slow down. Remember, to succeed you need to take one step at a time. Don't start skipping the important parts.

CHAPTER TWELVE

HOW DO YOU GET TO...?
PRACTICE, PRACTICE, PRACTICE

Theory can leave questions unanswered, but practice has to come up with something.

Mason Cooley

I walk back to my office feeling good about the morning. When I get there, I have a few vendor phone messages about past due payments and some business emails. I call them back and, as usual, the game of telephone tag begins. I've tried unsuccessfully to get all of our suppliers on an email format, but some people are still afraid of computers and won't even try communicating by email. We are all in a race between retirement and obsolescence, and some of these people just quit running and sit down.

I wonder what the payoff is in not using a computer; it is probably avoiding the discomfort of change.

Some of these people are only in their fifties. What are they going to do for the next twenty years?

I call Stan to find out how to contact Mr. Cluster. He says Cluster doesn't have an email address, but he does have a fax number and an office number. I get both and call Cluster's office.

On the first ring, I get the voice message of his assistant, who sounds as if he's being strangled. I laugh aloud when I hear, "Leave a message." There's no acknowledgement, no greeting, not even a request to keep the message short or to leave a number, not anything. "Leave a message"—that's it. I ask to be called back.

I want to walk the property but think better of that idea. I'll get the same questions about RCL from each department head I see and that will not be very efficient or effective. RCL should be discussed when we have enough time.

I'm restless and decide to see if I can find Rosie. When I get into the lobby, I spot him talking with a guest, probably arranging a run to the airport. The guest departs, happy as guests always are when dealing with Rosie. He greets me with a big smile. We chat for a few minutes about the weather, how the Panthers are doing, and how business has picked up recently. Then I get to the reason I came to see him.

"Rosie, I don't think I've ever seen anyone who seems to enjoy their work as much as you do. What's your secret?" He flashes that big smile and looks pleased that I asked.

"My dad was a good man," Rosie says. "He worked long and hard, made it through some tough times financially, but he never had a job he liked. That wore hard on him. It made him a miserable human being. When I was about to graduate from school, I asked him about it. He said, 'Don't set your standard of living and then look for a job to meet it. Oh, no. What you want to do is find the kind of work you like and set your standard of living to match it. A man that ain't happy in his work ain't gonna be happy in his life.' Best advice I ever got. I'm a happy man and nobody's going to change that by waving a little extra money in front of me. No, the devil might tempt me on some things, but not on that."

I'm surprised by what he has said and especially his conviction. "Lucky man you are, having a father that passed along advice like that. And you're smart to follow it. So why work in a hotel and why this hotel? Why are you so happy in this job?"

"Well, that's easy. I'm real good at what I do and I love doing it. Not good, but real good. Not like, but love. I don't have to depend on nobody around here to make me happy or to do my job."

"Thanks for talking to me, Rosie. I'm really happy you're here. Not happy, but really happy." We both laugh. "You're a good man."

As I turn to walk away, my mind is racing. The bell captain in my hotel has just given me a lesson in motivation. I walk back to my office as quickly as I can, sit down, and take notes. Rosie said, "I'm real good at what I do." Okay, that's the skill element. He has the skills for the job, and even more important, he *knows* he has the skills for the job.

The next thing was "I don't have to depend on anyone to make me happy or do my job." He's saying he's happy doing what he's doing, that his job satisfaction doesn't come from others. He's pursuing personal payoffs, but he doesn't have to depend on anyone else to get them. So where do they come from? Well, they must come from the work he does: interacting with guests, providing a service, making people's stays with us special, that kind of thing. Put differently, he has a very high level of interest in his job.

I reach over to the corner of my desk and pick up the Spencer book. I think Spencer calls it intrinsic satisfaction. I remember from my college days that

McClelland discussed n-Achievement and intrinsic satisfactions. Yep, there it is in the index. I quickly flip to the page and read.

Well, Spencer's explanation is a little too professorial for me. I explain it this way: People who have a high interest and skill level in a task collect rewards for their performance. Therefore, by definition, they receive personal payoffs doing their jobs. When that occurs, work life is good.

It seems to me that one of the most important things leaders can do is put people in the right jobs. Rosie is testimony to that idea. When people are in jobs they love, they just want to be left alone to do their work. And they do it right.

Spencer talked about this in the D.C. seminar. I had forgotten, but Rosie's comments remind me of how important being in the right job can be.

So what am I going to do? First of all, I'm not going to forget this time. The main thing is to put this into action. That means starting with my department heads. Are all of them in the right jobs? The best way to find out is in the one-on-one sessions that I already am planning to have with each of them.

I start putting together a plan for conducting the Reality Check one-on-one discussions. First, I'll have everyone take the SISP. That will give me a baseline about their perceived skill levels in eleven areas and their corresponding interest in those areas. Their responses will be compared to others working in the same areas. The managers can then see how others in the industry rate their skills and interests in the various departments.

Once scored, the SISP will provide anyone who takes it with a useful summary of his or her self-perceived skill level and some elements of their personal payoffs (interest levels). After all, it doesn't matter how good you are on any one task if you have no payoff (or worse, if you have a negative payoff) in performing the task. Armed with information about two of the elements in RCL, a company president, a general manager, or a department head need only determine the other payoffs an individual has and what that person thinks of the reward system.

Next, I will schedule a one-on-one session with each of my department heads. No more than one a day. I'm new to this and don't want to screw up because I'm tired. Who to start with? The potentially easy ones or the most difficult? As I list the departments, I jot down notes on my preconceived notions about the department and the particular person I have placed in that position. While some people like Vance were transferred to the hotel when we opened, I have hired more than half of the managers working at the Diamond.

1.   Housekeeping: Hard work, reasonable pay, not much of a chance for advancement unless you really push to get ahead. My executive housekeeper, Helen, is as hard working as anyone I know. She will be interested in moving up.

2.   Maintenance: Hard work, appropriate salary level. Needs strong technical skills and the willingness to be on call at all hours. Vance will not like this Reality Check at all and, if I schedule him, he will find reason after reason to miss the session.

3.   Food & Beverage: Another difficult position with appropriate rewards. Position, if handled properly, is a gateway into the GM ranks. Requires long hours and ability to control a multitude of costs. Dean is already looking for his next promotion.

4. Sales and Catering: The job that has the highest pressure and is most misunderstood. Other employees see only the special luncheons when site visits are scheduled, trips to major cities, and attendance at Chamber and HTA meetings. The individual that exhibits both the sales and marketing skills necessary and the administrative skills required of a big sales office is almost assured offers to move up in the organization. Don't know if Tracy is interested in being a GM.

5. Front Desk: The frontline of any hotel. The front desk manager takes the heat from the guests and other departments. When guests are disappointed or angry, they dial zero first. Ken is very adept at handling the people pressure and the reporting requirements of the hotel and the home office. He's very new at this position and needs more leadership experience, but I just know he wants to move up NOW.

6. General Manager: To be determined.

7. Security: Not a very high status position and, for all intents and purposes, not a good place to move up in the hotel business. We really need them but I'm afraid the payoffs are not great.

8. Accounting: What can I say about a job that requires the patience of a saint and the tenacity of a bulldog? My guy is a good accountant and handles disgruntled vendors and guests with the same calm attitude. His preferences will be to stay with the numbers

rather than the people, but he handles both well.

9. Human Resources: No longer just a people department, HR has been turned into a department responsible for dealing with all of the local, state, and federal government agencies. Our political leaders have interfered with almost everything imaginable in the work place. As a result, HR focuses more and more on paperwork and less and less on development and training. The tail has begun to wag the dog. Because there is a law or regulation covering almost every aspect of the world of work, I have three people who simply deal with the reports that have to be filed and payroll taxes that have to be paid on all sorts of activities. The HR director has to understand laws that even the people who pass them can't. Along with payroll and the required deductions, HR has to keep up with all of the changes that are made throughout the year. A high tolerance for ambiguity is required, but following all the rules can make anyone rigid. Sandra handles it all well, and I'm not sure if she is interested in moving up.

With my notes complete, I seal them in an envelope and place it in my out box to be put in the safe. Wonder how close my perceptions will be to the truths revealed by my Reality Check discussions.

I have Dean, the F & B director, on my mind, wondering what his next move will be. My guess is it will come soon, and I had better be prepared. I look at my watch.

The rush for lunch should be over. Now would be a good time to catch Ethel, the waitress that fits Dr.

168

Spencer's description in the story he told in the D.C. seminar. I'm almost positive she's the one. I'll soon find out.

When I get to the restaurant, she's telling her last guest goodbye. She waves me over and signals that a cup of coffee is on the way. She shows up in about sixty seconds and sets it on the table in front of me.

We engage in our usual chitchat for a couple of minutes before I move toward the subject I want to discuss. "I haven't talked to you much since the new restaurant manager came on board," I tell her.

She glances over her shoulder and scans the entire restaurant area. "No, you haven't. You been stayin' busy, I guess."

"Look, Ethel, we've known each other for a long time. I need you to be honest with me. How's it going?"

She makes another scan for effect, a quick peek over her shoulder, then says, "Well, not so good."

"What do you mean?"

"He's just different than Tony, you know. Tony took a real interest in everybody. He told you how he wanted you to do things, and he trusted you to do it. He was easy to talk to. If you had a problem, you could go to Tony and he'd fix it. It's not anything like that now."

I do not talk, creating a little tension with my silence. After thirty seconds or so, she continues.

"To be honest with you, everybody is about fed up with the new guy. He doesn't have the experience for a restaurant like this. Basically, he's in over his head. Acts as if he hates his job, too. Seems immature, insecure, and definitely paranoid about looking good. Afraid he'll lose his job, that's my opinion."

"Are people talking about leaving?"

"Only the best ones."

"That's the way it always is, isn't it? Ethel thinks. This is confidential, just between you and me, like always."

"Yeah, I know. Thanks."

As she walks away, I get a mental image of Dr. Spencer standing at the front of the seminar room in D.C. and hearing him say, "If someone is performing poorly, someone is letting them get by with it." I know now that when you let negative behavior continue, you are rewarding by ignoring.

I need to schedule the SISP. I go through my notes and find the web site, www.DirectionsForHospitality.com. I get online and pick up the site. The home page indicates that an individual can take the profile online. The resulting summary profile, which will be provided via email, will compare the respondent with others actually working in the various functional areas of a hotel.

I pay for eleven respondents with my credit card. I receive a confirmation email that contains my Login ID, our passwords, and an explanation of the process that we will follow.

An overall summary for all respondents will be returned to the hotel, and the individuals will receive their personal results, unless they request otherwise.

I prepare a general memo that explains the process and write in the individual passwords assigned to each department head. I ask in the memo that they fill out the profile when they have at least an hour of uninterrupted time, preferably at home. The value of the profile will be a function of the accuracy of the responses they provide. I thank them in advance for taking the time to complete the profile and remind them that this is the first step in the process of better understanding themselves and others.

I really like this kind of thing. There is something fascinating (maybe a payoff?) about a deeper understanding of human behavior. Not only will it help my professional career, but it will make the rest of my life a little easier. I can't wait to try out RCL.

I drop the memos in their respective boxes and go back to my office. So far, there are no calls from Spencer or Cluster. It is after two o'clock and I need to work out. Just as I am about to leave for the club, Dean, my F & B director, walks in.

He drops down in a chair and says, "I guess we need to talk."

I say, "Hello," and laugh.

He gives me a half-hearted smile that doesn't last.

"Talk to me," I say.

"I have a feeling you know about Louis."

"I have a feeling about him, but that's it. Why don't you tell me what I need to know?"

"Two things: He's a bad hire, and I keep hoping for the best."

"What are you planning to do about it?"

"I'm not sure. What do you think I should do?" he says with a bewildered look on his face. This is so typical of him. He does a great job in every area of his job, but he'd rather stand on a street corner all day counting cars than deal with people problems. "Dean, this is your decision."

"Do you think RCL applies here? I mean, do you think it would help me get to a good decision?"

"I believe it would provide you the information you need to make the right decision. However, this is serious. You don't have much time."

"I just got this memo from my box, the one about the...What's it called?" He quickly scans the paper in his hand. "Oh, yeah, the SISP. Do you think that would help with my problem with Louis?"

"Hey, it's been paid for and it only takes a little time. What do you have to lose? Why don't you and Louis both take it?"

"Okay, I'll get started on this right away."

"Dean, you will handle this well. Just keep me informed." He gets up to leave and I say, "I'm beginning to think that one of the most important things a leader can do is put people in the right jobs. And that sometimes, because of the pressure of turnover, we hire warm bodies for jobs they may not be suited for."

He turns to walk away and looks over his shoulder with a pained expression on his face. "I'm learning that the hard way." And he is gone.

This is great. There are so many opportunities to use RCL. Apparently, my managers can see the application for their own problems. I haven't been this excited about my work in a long time. I'm getting more and more payoffs every day.

I arrive at BodyCheck around three thirty and change into my workout clothes. After an hour and ten minutes of treadmill work, I feel great. My mind is clear and that good feeling I get from really pushing myself is there. My endorphins have kicked in. That's a great payoff and life is good. I take a shower, dress, and head back to the hotel.

Traffic is starting to build and I get to the hotel just in time. I plan on staying through the rush hour and then going home.

I'm disappointed to learn that I have had no calls. I want to get that information to the VP of Operations and I want to hear from Cluster. I start thinking about Vance. Fact is, if he doesn't want to go through RC, that's fine. He works hard and does a great job. I don't want to force him into a situation where he's uncomfortable. He ain't broke; I'm not going to try to fix him.

As if on cue, Vance walks in, chewing on a big unlit cigar and holding the SISP memo.

He says, "Do I have to do this?"

"Sure, it will be fun." I'm going to have some fun with him before I let him off.

"Come on. Don't make me do this stuff. I'm busy and besides, it sounds like a bunch of psychobabble that will be a waste of time."

I smile. "Don't hold back. Tell me what you really think." Now he knows he's won. Watch him move to get this out of the way.

Vance smiles. "Thanks, and by the way, I saved you ten thousand dollars today."

"How's that?"

"I fixed the leak in the second tower boiler instead of buying a new boiler."

I wonder how much it actually cost me to save ten thousand dollars. I know we had to bring in a licensed maintenance company. "Thanks. That will be a big help. Should we plan on asking for a new one during capital time?"

"No, they said that the fix should hold for another three or four years."

"Great, then that really is good news. What company did you use?"

"The guys from TRIMCO. We use them for all of our preventative maintenance work and they save us a bundle."

"Thanks for babysitting the thing last night, and call me when the TRIMCO guys show up again. I want to say thanks to them personally."

"You should really thank Frank Linker; he's the guy behind their good work."

"Give me his number and I'll call."

"You don't have to. He's a hands-on president. He'll be here."

"Okay, I will see him. Let me know."

Vance and I talk a few more minutes and then he leaves to get back to his crew. He has eight men in the Maintenance Department who have been with him for years. You can't buy the kind of loyalty that Vance gets from his people. He's a no-nonsense, get-the-job-done-now kind of boss; but they love and respect him. He can do anything and makes sure you know it, too.

As he leaves, I check my email and voicemail one more time. No luck. I'll have to wait until tomorrow. I pick up my notes on RCL and head for the door.

It is already dark and feels as if the temperature has dropped twenty degrees. The clouds push down and reflect the lights from the downtown area. The air feels heavy, almost wet. It's a perfect night for some snow. I get in my car and by the time I pull out of the Diamond parking lot, I'm cold. I leave the heat on auto at seventy-three degrees and turn on the seat warmer.

I wonder how Stan is doing with the Cluster problem. He and I had agreed to present Cluster with the financial facts about his little race week party. With two of us, Cluster should be less likely to intimidate Stan. I'll go over to the Hampton tomorrow morning.

CHAPTER THIRTEEN

BUT WILL RCL WORK AT MY HOTEL?

Nothing is so threatening to conventional values as a man who does not want to work or does not want to work at a challenging job, and most people are disturbed if a man in a well-paying job indicates ambivalence or dislike toward it.

Alice S. Rossi

I know that RCL is a great tool for the Diamond Creek Inn. We have the financial resources and support staff to handle all of the data collection necessary to implement RCL. I wonder if it can work at a place like the Hampton with an owner like Cluster. He doesn't like spending any money for employee development, but as I think about the cost, it's actually quite minimal.

175

Once the general manager is comfortable with RCL, the rest is simple. First, determine the interest and skill level of your people; using the SISP makes it easy. Second, determine the organization's reward system, and third, identify the personal payoffs of the individuals in question. The biggest expense is the time necessary to do it right.

However, once a manager at any level realizes that RCL is the most effective and efficient way to get things done with other people, the benefits more than outweigh the costs. When managers recognize that the first element in RCL, the SISP, can also be used for hiring and development decisions, they are more than willing to employ the concept in leading others.

RCL is flexible because managers who are comfortable with it are able to use their own judgments as to what specific behavioral approaches they choose to employ. RCL does not require major behavioral changes on the part of good leaders—rather, it provides information for those managers so that they can lead more effectively.

I know that RCL does not claim to change people. I am also convinced that trying to change what has occurred is a complete waste of time. People hear and say, "It is what it is," all the time, but few actually live by those words. More and more we tend to wish for things to be better or for things to stop happening without us doing anything about the cause.

RCL provides guidelines for positive leadership, while not claiming to be all things to all people. I like the approach: RCL can help me at work, period. (However, I do believe that the major elements in RCL could also be used in interpersonal relationships.)

I walk into the lobby of the Hampton Inn and immediately sense something isn't right. It is amazing how the atmosphere in a hotel lobby can generate positive or negative feelings. I've always believed that you can correlate the attitude and personality of the general manager with that of the front desk personnel. If the manager is productive and is receiving payoffs with his position, it reflects in his people. If, on the other hand, he's tense or under duress, the employees exhibit similar behavior. Moreover, if he is seen as only doing the necessary minimum or has an attitude of disinterest, the staff emulates those actions, too. Leadership, good or bad, influences behavioral variables in an organization. I'm beginning to sound like Spencer, and that is a payoff for me.

I ask Carol, a GSR, if Mr. Wohart is available, and she calls the office to find out. I know that Stan has a lobby monitor in his office and already knows I'm at the desk. I figure he must be tied up with something and, sure enough, Carol says he'll be with me in a minute. I pick up a *USA Today*, get a cup of coffee, and sit down to wait.

In a few minutes, Stan and Fred, the back office manager, come out of the small GM's office. Word has it that Cluster built this tiny room because he believes a GM should keep moving and not have too nice of a place to sit and think. Another genius idea! As they walk toward me, I can feel the tension in the air. We all exchange chitchat and Fred leaves. I look directly at Stan, "What was that all about?"

"I just don't know what to do with Fred."

I suggest we get a cup of coffee and sit in the breakfast area. It is ten o'clock and the lobby is empty. Commercial hotels are normally like that from 9:30 a.m. until around 4:00 p.m. most weekdays.

I walk to the back of the breakfast seating area while Stan checks on something at the desk. I notice two things as he walks back. One, his shoulders are tense and his face has a deep frown; I have the feeling he left for a minute to try to compose himself. Two, it has started to snow, a very light, almost melting, immediately wet snow. That brings joy to my heart. He sits down.

"So can I help?" I ask.

"I hate bothering you with all my problems."

"That's why they pay me the big bucks."

He laughs and says, "I know but first it was Cluster and his race week screw-up and now this."

"What's 'this'?"

"Well, I found out that Fred let one of his front desk people go on vacation again right in the middle of race week. We need everyone's help and Fred, once again, lets me down by just telling me half the story. In fact, he went out of his way to lead me to believe that vacations were all taken care of for the year. When I asked where Randy was three days later, I was told that he went on vacation Friday and would not return until a week from Monday. I just don't know what to do with Fred. He's a good man, but I can't trust what he says anymore."

"That is a big problem, but maybe we can use RCL to solve it." I suggest that we work through the problem using the three key elements of RCL.

Stan looks skeptical. "Okay. I don't know what else to do."

"Good. Let's get started. There are three major factors that can influence the behavior of an employee. First is their level of interest and skill in performing particular tasks or functions. Second, all relevant behavior that is rewarded is repeated. We'll talk more about this later. Finally, there are the personal payoffs they get from performing the way they do." Stan looks confused and I smile. "It's a lot easier than it initially seems. Let me show you.

"First, does Fred have an interest in the tasks and does he believe he can perform them? That is, does he have the skills necessary to be a good back office manager?"

"I think he loves what he does, and I know he's very good at numbers," Stan says. "I very seldom have a problem, and when I do, Fred can fix it quickly."

"You think he loves what he does, but you're not sure? If you don't know, there is a great profile that can help you understand where your people are coming from relative to their perceived interests and skills. It's the SISP, but we will assume for now that you don't need it in this case. Okay, let's move on."

I continue, "Second, you have to know that all behavior that is rewarded is repeated. If you've been rewarding unacceptable behavior, then you're encouraging behavior that isn't productive."

"How can that be?"

"If you ignore behavior that you deem inappropriate, that's the same thing as encouraging the action. People see rewards in different ways. For example, when you don't correct behavior, it becomes acceptable. Have you ever had employees say they were surprised by your anger?"

"Well, yes."

"That's the reason they were surprised. Ignoring can be a positive or negative reward. You didn't correct them initially and then, when you got fed up and took action, to them it was out of the blue. I assume this isn't the first time Fred has disappointed you by seeming to hide things from you. Have you mentioned it at all to him?"

Stan looked into his cup and softly said, "Well, no, not really."

"So part of the puzzle is that Fred may not know he's doing something wrong."

With that, Stan sits up. "He has to know that everyone works race week."

"Maybe he has something that overrides your expectation of him."

"What could that be?" he asks.

"That leads me to the third factor in the determination of why people behave the way they do. Simply stated, 'People pursue personal payoffs.'"

Stan thinks about that for a moment. "That seems like a harsh view of people."

"Not really. It's a realistic approach to understanding what motivates people to do things. Personal payoffs are as varied as people are different. For years, social scientists have tried to put the 'motivations' of people in categories and boxes. The truth is that each person enters a situation and interacts in that environment. Their behavior is based on acquiring personal payoffs: happiness, money, feeling safe, risk taking, being directed, autonomy, and the list goes on. Some people and their payoffs change and adapt over time. What's important to understand is that people have their own payoffs, and the only way you can determine what they are is to observe and ask."

"How do I do that? Just go up and ask them to list their payoffs?"

"No, first you use the power of observation. I bet if you tried you could put together a few of the payoffs that Fred exhibits every day."

"I'll need some time to think about that."

"Stan, one word of caution. If you're not careful, two things will occur. One, you'll put this aside because it's easier not to do anything, then, when it happens again, you'll blow your cork. Two, the pressures of running a 120-room property with a limited staff can bury you in work, another reason to let this approach slide.

"However, I can assure you that if you try RCL, you and the hotel will benefit. Why not work on the problem now and give me a call tomorrow with what you think you have? Don't worry about getting it right the first time. We will go through the steps together and both learn."

Stan thanks me and we talk about the hotel in general. He and I walk the property, and I comment on how good the landscaping looks. We inspect a few rooms and I notice some "old dirt" and comment to Stan. He tells me he's having a difficult time getting housekeepers because of the competition for labor. I suggest he start inspecting five rooms a day and that I'll come by soon and do the same thing. If our housekeepers don't think we care about cleanliness, why should they? This is yet another example of behavior that has been sanctioned by inattention. What I realize, however, is that this is both Stan's inattention and mine.

As we continue to walk the property, I realize Stan needs some expectation clarification just as Fred does. People have to know what they are responsible for getting done. I give him the benefit of the doubt because he has to deal with Cluster.

Stan talks a good game, but his performance does not always match. There are negative things about his leadership but, because his bottom line numbers are improving, I've let him slide. On the other hand, maybe I haven't known how to handle this kind of situation. RCL provides me with a way of judging performance that goes beyond the monthly profit and loss statement.

I want to get away and think about Stan. Whatever kind of a jerk Cluster is, he's paying five percent per month to have his hotel properly managed, and I'm responsible to him and Matrix. Stan and I talk a little about sales and his forecasts for the quarter, and then I head back to the Diamond.

The Hampton and Diamond Creek Inn are about ten miles apart, but in Charlotte traffic at four thirty in the afternoon, that could take thirty minutes to drive. As I leave the Hampton I notice the parking lot actually has a dusting of snow and I can see my tire tracks. I drive the back roads to the hotel and get there without any trouble. I listen to the radio and hear that the forecasters are predicting some accumulation. When I hear four to five inches I actually cheer. How nuts is that—a guy in a car by himself cheering for snowfall?

When I return to the Diamond, I notice my hotel is as busy as I've seen it in quite a while, and I smile. Every

181

place I look there is activity. A few guests stand in line to check in, but the line is moving at an acceptable rate. Porters and bellmen are working the front entrance, and the happy hour crowd is a good size and growing.

I walk through the restaurants and notice servers getting ready for the night. The ballroom is alive with banquet servers and backup people. I talk to everyone in housekeeping, and as I walk back to my office, I notice smiles, joking, and laughter. When the hotel is busy, our people are excited and, I believe, proud. The hotel business is exciting because the pace is fast and ever changing. In addition, people who love the business are proud of being associated with a winner. In our business, like others, busy is winning.

Even the lingo used by people in the hospitality industry is unique. Big, unexpected dinner or breakfast crowds are described by employees as, "we got slammed." When we have great occupancy numbers, we often say that "we had to walk people." Words like *imprest*, *pick-ups*, and *bookings* are part of the nomenclature known by hotel people.

I smile to myself. Days like this are one of the big payoffs I get from operating the Diamond. The smooth flow of people and purposes is incredible for anyone interested in leadership. I'm basking in the payoff of successful management when my cell phone rings.

It's Stan, and he's excited. "I think I know why Fred behaves the way he does with his people." Before I can respond, he says, "His payoff is being liked—by everyone—and some of them take advantage of him. He lets Randy, the laziest GSR we have, go on vacation so Randy will like him. His payoff is believing that his good intentions will be rewarded with being liked, although I know Randy will just take and take and never give back."

I smile. "I like your insight, Stan. Now we need to do one other thing."

"What's that?"

"We have to verify whether or not what you think is true."

"Oh, I guess that's right. How do I do that?"

"Well, you could ask Fred about his payoffs without being threatening."

"Should I try and find out from him, or do you want to do it?"

"No, you do it. Just remember, if you're right, he's going to be uncomfortable talking about a payoff that does not put him in a good light. In his world, he would prefer to cause disruption and additional expense rather than risk the disapproval of an employee who in your mind is both ungrateful and lazy."

"Wow, that's a lot of negative information for him. Do you think he can handle it? I really need him around here."

"More important, Stan, do you? And do you need him around there the way he is?"

"Well, no, not if he continues to act this way."

"Talk to him and let me know."

"Okay. I'll do that tomorrow morning."

"Have a good night. Talk to you in the morning."

Vance comes in dressed as if we were in an ice age. He says, "I'm going to start moving the snow, okay?"

"Man, Vance, I hate that. Why can't we just leave it? I know, I know, too many cars tomorrow to get anything done. Okay, go ahead. Have you heard the latest forecast?"

"Yeah, somewhere between three and four inches."

"I hear four to five."

"Nobody knows."

"You're right. Okay, get to the snow and then get home. It's been a long day for you."

"Yeah, right." He will be here until ten tonight just in case.

I leave the hotel and head home. Now the flakes have turned drier, and I can hear them hitting the car.

The headlights at even slow speeds make it seem like a blizzard. Traffic is moving at a slower rate, and I sit back and enjoy the scene being played out in front of me.

I like the idea of using RCL when I can observe its effectiveness from a distance. If Stan can get the relevant information he needs to make a decision about the problem with Fred, he is more than halfway there. Making and implementing his decision is the next and most important step. While that sounds like simple common sense, some people hesitate, or worse, put off doing what needs to be done. Stan is one of those people who replace action with talk. His favorite expression is, "I was going to..." He tells me about a tough decision he has made and weeks later I find out nothing has been done. I know that I need to think more about Stan and his performance in terms of RCL.

That leads me to think about my managers and RCL. Before I get home, my head is spinning with things to do. Sometimes it drives me crazy not to be able to shut down work. However, I like what I'm doing, so I guess it's a payoff. Besides, it's only work when you would rather be doing something else.

The next morning I drive through about three inches of snow, getting to the Diamond around seven o'clock. I have much to do today and hope to make some progress on RCL.

After saying hello to my people, I head to my office with a cup of coffee. I make a list of the people I want to work with using RCL. Stan is number one on the list for a couple of reasons. One, he does have some negatives that need to be addressed, and two, I haven't done anything about his behavior. I can't forget that he also has some positives that need encouragement.

Maybe I've procrastinated because I didn't have a way to get at what I'm feeling. That's the great thing about RCL. It adds structure and substance to your "feelings" and provides a way to collect information about the elements that influence real behavior.

I remember that when real behavior differs from expected behavior, problems can occur. How often have you said to yourself, "I have a funny feeling about this person"? RCL can help clarify your feelings and put them into a logical format. Maybe your feeling is just that, a feeling; or maybe it is really intuition.

I call Stan at the Hampton. It's funny how he's never in early and mentions how late he works whenever he sees me. I never check on him. I believe that it's not the number of hours you spend at your job; it's the results you obtain. As I think about his hours, I decide to ask Stan about his typical day. It's a fair question and I need to know.

Within three minutes, Stan calls. Obviously, the GSR called him right after I called. I ask him to take the SISP today and to plan to meet me around four. He asks if there is a problem, and I quickly explain that I'm employing RCL as a way of conducting an evaluation of him. I also explain that part of our discussion will be centered on his future career development needs. He seems satisfied and tells me he plans to meet with Fred this morning. I remind him that the SISP will take less than an hour and that it will be an important part of our meeting.

Around eight o'clock, Tracy walks in and asks me if I have some time. I really want to start on my RCL project, but she seems nervous and I worry that she is accepting another offer. She gets them all the time.

"Don't you dare tell me you're leaving," I say.

She laughs. "Don't worry, I know the 'family' rules."

"Ah, yet another Mafia reference. But whatever works. So what do you want?"

"I need some help with the second part of Reality Check."

"What kind of help?"

"I'm not sure I understand what the rewarded behavior element really means. Can you help?"

"I think I can at least give you my interpretation of what that element entails. Do you want some coffee?"

"No thanks."

"Tracy, my understanding is that this part involves two major concepts. Rewarded behavior is repeated, and the organization's reward system is the most effective behavior-training program. Don't confuse effective with good. Now, I sound like some college professor."

"No, go on. You're really good at explaining this stuff."

"Yeah, I know. Okay, one concept is that all behavior that is rewarded is repeated. The obvious conclusion is that behavior that is not rewarded will soon not be repeated. You could even say that good behavior that is ignored will also decrease in occurrence. When people exhibit bad behavior and are allowed to continue, they perceive that as a reward. People need to know that the good they are doing at work will be rewarded and that unacceptable behavior will not be allowed to continue. Remember, we have established that if they are interested in their jobs and believe they have the necessary skills, the next bit of information we need is their perceptions of the reward system. And that leads me to the second concept. Tracy, as far as your people are concerned, you are the Diamond Creek Inn."

"How can that be?"

"Because for most employees, their direct supervisor, manager, leader, or whatever you want to call the person, represents the company. How you behave with your people is a major factor in how they will perceive the entire reward system of this hotel. Although there are a number of factors that make up the company's reward system—compensation, profit sharing, working conditions, health benefits, recognition, and promotion opportunities, just to name a few—you are the key to their perception."

I'm on a roll now. "If they believe you will reward their behavior fairly, they will perceive the company's entire reward system as being fair. A good leader can influence employees to accept even marginal rewards for some period of time, while a bad leader can negate all the good a company is trying to do relative to the reward system. Unless people perceive that their good and bad behavior will be recognized, their motivation to perform will diminish over time. Enough?"

Tracy smiles, "Yes, and I caught that arrogant comment about how you knew you were good." We both laugh and she says that she now has a better understanding of the role she plays in the reward system.

Stan calls at nine o'clock. From the excitement in his voice, I know things have gone well. He tells me he called Fred into his office and they talked for about an hour. The conversation went extremely well; and Fred, after a while, did acknowledge that he may be protecting his employees too much. They discussed those employees who take advantage of Fred's behavior and came up with Randy as the one most likely not to appreciate the favors that Fred does for him. Although Fred is not about to give up on helping his employees, from now on, he will balance the rewards he offers with the benefits to the hotel and his performance.

I ask Stan if he believes Fred will change. Stan indicates that now that he knows what payoff Fred is interested in, he will monitor his actions until he feels comfortable.

"Stan, you haven't answered the question."

"Oh, well, I'm sure he understands the situation."

"Why are you sure?"

There is a long pause, and I outwait him. Finally, he blurts out that no, in fact, he is not sure that Fred will change.

I explain to him that, as far as I'm concerned, the only thing that happened was that he and Fred talked for

187

a while. Stan sounds uncomfortable and tells me that he thinks Fred will change. Again, I ask why. He doesn't have a response, so I suggest he do two things: First, clearly explain to Fred why his behavior is not acceptable. Second, explain to Fred that any more surprises like this last one and he will have a significant problem with him.

I ask Stan if he understands. He says yes, although I think he senses a change in my behavior toward him. Maybe that will help in our meeting this afternoon.

Stan tells me he really appreciates the help (yeah, right) and that he is going to start using RCL just as soon as race week is over. I laugh, "Good, Stan." Amazing how people want to believe RCL is more work and that they have to wait until they have time to start using it as a leadership tool. Oh, well, one step at a time.

I get back to my day and things go so well that by the afternoon, I realize I will have time to work out with my trainer. I'm in my office when Stan walks in for our four o'clock meeting. He smiles at my workout clothes because I normally dress in a suit and tie when at the Diamond. I expect my people to look professional, so I really have no choice.

Stan and I talk about Fred, who is confused about his role as the back office manager. I ask why, and Stan responds, "He said that he thought he was responsible for the scheduling of his people. And I had to agree and didn't know how to explain how we got off track."

I thought for a moment. "Stan, we have a problem of too much ownership of the job." He looked puzzled. "In this situation, the idea that a manager should own the responsibility of his position has been taken too far. While it's important for employees to feel that the tasks they have are their responsibility, in some situations people take too much discretion in deciding what is in their purview to decide. In this case, Fred believes that he knows best when it comes to scheduling. That is compounded when he doesn't know he behaves in a way that seeks approval of his employees. Finally, because you did not express your disapproval with previous scheduling problems, it was easy for him to continue to try and please the employees. What you did today was show Fred that, first, you know that a big personal payoff for him is the approval of his subordinates and that he seems willing to jeopardize his performance for the sake of that approval. We know that Fred has other payoffs, and you've provided him with an opportunity to express those that he knows about. You let him know you were on his side with this problem and that together you could resolve the issue. Second, his behavior relative to scheduling time off for his employees during your busiest time will have negative payoffs—in this case, your disapproval. So, you've established that his current behavior won't be rewarded and that a change in his payoff priorities is essential. He knows he has to put Hampton Hotel objectives before employee approval."

Stan thinks for a moment. "That sounds good when you say it," he says, "but at the time I was talking to Fred, I got confused. How do I learn to express myself confidently? In fact, I get confused whenever I have to talk to people about their poor performance." He sounds panicked. "Can you help me?"

I decide right there to back off from his evaluation and do some leadership training on my own. I'm convinced that if Stan knows how to use RCL, he will be more able to deal with all his employee behavior situations.

"Stan, let's not go over your evaluation right now. Let's talk about what RCL can do for you."

"Good, I can use all the help I can get."

"Okay, let me try to explain why RCL can give you the confidence you need to deal with situations where employee or supervisor behavior does not match your expectations."

Stan looks hopeful. "Sounds good. I'm ready."

"RCL provides you with an understanding of the three elements that are the major factors in the difference between expected behavior and real behavior. The first element is levels of interest and skill in the essential functions of a hotel. A leader can choose to use the SISP or estimate those. I suggest you use the profile when you can. It's the first thing that adds confidence to your attitude about modifying behavior.

"The second element involves rewarded behavior and the organization's reward system. You can employ the *Schilagi Organization Survey* (SOS), or if you think you have the experience, you can extrapolate the rewards from your knowledge of the situation.

"Third is personal payoff identification. This is a matter of asking your people what they see as the payoffs they most want to pursue. As simple as that sounds, you'll be gaining some critical information you need to make a judgment about what motivates people to behave the way they do in the work place."

Stan smiles as if I have given him a gift, and I guess I have. I've given him the one thing that all leaders need at one time or another—a direction to take when times get tough. If you don't believe in what you're saying about an individual's behavior, how can you expect the person to agree? Potentially good leaders fail because of nagging doubts about their perceptions relative to individual behavior. They don't have an established direction to follow and, therefore, feel uncertain about how to proceed. (I have a very good friend, David Campbell, who wrote a great book titled, *If You Don't Know Where You're Going, You'll Probably End Up Somewhere Else.*)

RCL provides anyone who takes the time to learn a storehouse of information about employee perceptions and behavior. When you know what the interests, skills, rewards, and payoffs are for people, you know why they behave the way they do at work.

"Stan, having RCL information at your disposal will give you the confidence you need. When people understand that you aren't just guessing at why they behave the way they do, they will appreciate the attention and importance you place on their work behavior.

"It's one thing to say, 'You are important to this organization'; it's another to take the time to show that they are. People want to hear about themselves, and you as a leader can provide that payoff for a small investment."

"I understand, and you're right," Stan says. "I need to start now with RCL and not wait until after the race."

"Good. I hope you do get started. And I want you to know that my discussions with you that are centered on RCL information are just one of a number that I'm doing. I plan on covering all my people here and you are the normal extension of that plan."

Stan lights up. "Whew, I'm glad to hear that. I thought I might be in trouble."

Trying but failing to keep a straight face, I say, "And what have you been doing to think you would be in trouble?" We both laugh and Stan heads back to the Hampton.

I slip out my back office door and head home. It's almost six, and I've had a great day. It's dark and cold, and now I'm not in the mood to work out. There is a little snow left on some of the side streets, and I am ready to find out what's going on in the world.

CHAPTER FOURTEEN

YOU DIDN'T JUST MISS THE BOAT... YOU MISSED THE DOCK

Let me never fall into the vulgar mistake of dreaming that I am persecuted whenever I am contradicted.

Ralph Waldo Emerson

It takes me about thirty minutes to get home. Traffic is slow, but I do not push the issue and create unnecessary tension. I play a Michael Bublé CD and sing along. It is amazing how much I sound like him with the right volume on a twelve-speaker, thousand-watt stereo system. As I pull into my driveway, my cell phone rings. I don't recognize the number but break my rule of not answering unrecognized calls after 6:00 p.m. I hope it's Spencer, not Cluster. I don't need to deal with Cluster this late at night.

It's Spencer. "Hi, how has your day been?" I ask. I have always been curious about what people like him do, how they spend their time, and what payoffs they get from what they do.

"I've conducted a seminar all day. I'm just getting to my emails and phone calls," he responds. We chat as I walk into the house. "Do you have time to talk?" he asks.

"Absolutely."

I go through my normal routine of lighting the house but wait to change clothes. Instead, I take out some notepaper and a pencil and listen.

"About the seminar for Matrix," he says, "you asked how much time I'd need. It takes two days to bring a group of twenty people up to speed on RCL." I knew from his seminar I attended in D.C. that by a day he meant starting at nine o'clock, lunch from twelve thirty until two, and ending somewhere between four and four thirty. There would also be two fifteen-minute breaks.

"A group of professionals can master the concepts of RCL in a day," he says. "However, I would caution you that mastering the concepts and applying the theory can be quite different."

I laugh. "Let me assure you. I fully understand that knowing the elements of RCL is one thing and knowing them well enough to use them requires practice."

"Exactly. If you want this to work, you can't treat this like a hobby. You have to be serious about mastering the RCL concepts. And your people need to know you are serious about their participation."

"What about cost?"

"Well, the normal rate for a Reality Check for Leaders seminar is $475 per person, but because I'm new to the hotel business, why don't we do this one for $300 each. You understand, that is with a twenty-person minimum class size."

"Okay. Are there any other costs associated with the seminar?"

"I'll have expenses for travel and, of course, my room and meals. I will give everyone a copy of RCL, but you should also consider the cost of rooms and meals for the participants."

"Do you autograph the books?"

He laughs. "I will if you want. How do you hotel people handle rooms and meals?"

"We charge a rate that covers the cost of cleaning the room and pay for meals at the employee rate. Programs, seminars, and general manager meetings are held at a different property each time. That keeps one hotel from having to take all of the just-breakeven business."

"I see," he says.

"I don't know which hotel is up next in the rotation, but I can find out when I present this time and cost information you've given me to my VP, Dana Long. She's the decision maker on this issue. She seemed interested when I presented what I had learned in Washington."

"I will be happy to answer any questions she has. "Have her call me if she wants."

"Okay."

"Thanks for getting me into Matrix."

"I appreciate your willingness to work with us. I feel better and better about how RCL can help our general managers become better leaders."

"So tell me," he says, "what is your payoff for doing all this work?"

I think for a minute and say, "I'll have to get back to you on that, but my first response is that I like learning new ideas. More important, when the idea has potential to help me be a better leader, I really get interested. And the brownie points I will get at Matrix when this works don't hurt a bit."

"Good reasons, all of them, and I like it that you can call your payoffs up that fast."

"I haven't thought about it much, but I bet it's more difficult to use RCL with some people than with others."

He laughs, "Some people are impossible."

"What do you do then?"

"It's simple. Some people make your work world better by just going away."

I have Cluster in mind. He is not someone I could fire. Matrix could, but I doubt they would give up the fees. "I have one of those impossible people. Do you have time to listen to the problem?"

"Nope."

I'm so stunned I laugh out loud. He has got to be kidding!

He says, "Well, it's late, so you have a good night and I will look forward to hearing from you."

I say good night and we hang up.

Wow, there is a guy that has his personal payoffs clearly defined. Instead of talking for what would have been at least another hour, he calls it a day. It is 8:00 p.m. and I bet he's been working since six this morning. It's been a long day and it's time for me to stop, too.

I go to the kitchen and remember I had taken a steak out of the freezer. By the time I get the grill ready, cook the steak and make a salad, it will be nine o'clock. Forget that. What kind of soup do I have? Looks like it will be tomato soup and grilled cheese. More often than not, this is how my dinners turn out.

KNOWING YOU

If you refuse to accept your feelings about a loss, you will never rid yourself of emotional pain. Lack of acceptance can lead to chronic negative emotions.

Since Gail died, I have made my workdays longer and my time at home shorter. My dinners are a blur of last minute decisions with the primary goal of getting them over with. I pay one of the hotel's housekeepers to clean the house once a week. Brenda repeatedly says that although she can use the money, she thinks that once every two weeks or even once a month is enough. I like not thinking about cleaning more than I like the money, so I have her come once a week.

I sit at the kitchen table, watch most of a *Seinfeld* episode and eat dinner. This house is way too big. I think it's close to five thousand square feet. Why am I still here? Because like other things in my personal life I have just shut down and not made a decision.

Last year on Thanksgiving Day, Gail decided to take a nap, after another great Thanksgiving lunch. When she did not come into my study by six, I went to get her. She had died in her sleep. I still am numb with the shock and grief. As with any sudden unexpected death there was an autopsy and a brief police investigation. The pathologist could find no real cause of death and ended his report with the standard "we don't know" answer: her heart stopped. I wonder every day what could have happened. The fact is that I have to stop trying to change what cannot be changed.

Maybe a new smaller house would be a good idea. Maybe I will move to a condo and have all that landscaping done by some association. Could I find one that has the same features as this house, only smaller? Maybe I'll start looking after I get this RCL seminar nailed down. Maybe.

The personal decisions in my life have been put on hold. The only people I come into contact with are people at the hotel and at the health club. Most of our mutual friends moved on after a while. That was more my fault than theirs. It was uncomfortable for them, and I did not make it any easier by turning down invitation after invitation. On the other hand, maybe I did. From their perspective, it could not have been easy making small talk with the elephant in the room. I was not much fun to be with however hard they tried. So it seems understandable to me that they went on with their lives.

YOU SHOULD KNOW

If you spend your time focused on constraints, your behavior is controlled by frustration because of your inability to alter what has happened or what will happen.

I find that to be more comforting than disturbing. I guess that I have adopted the approach of Anthony Storr. His book, *Solitude: A Return to the Self*, is a great guide to the healing value of being alone during periods of mourning and stress. I agree with him when he writes, "It seems to me that what goes on in the human being when he is by himself is as important as what happens in his interactions with other people."

The attraction to solitude has not come about because of the loss of Gail. I have been, for as long as I can remember, a loner. In fact, when I was a kid, seventeen or so, I traveled the country hitchhiking alone. I always liked being alone.

When it comes to simple things like chit-chat, I often find myself in a bind as to what to say. I am always the last one to hear the latest gossip. Storr speculates that it would be interesting to know what portion of conversation consists of talking about the lives of other people. He contends that even the most intellectual persons are seldom averse to gossip, although they may affect to despise it. As Storr said, there is something to be said for superficial relationships. But that's enough of this heavy stuff for tonight. I think I will read for a while. It is very early in the morning when I finally fall asleep.

The sun is just coming up as I leave the house. The cold air feels good on my sand-filled eyes. There is much to do today, but first things first. I've put off thinking about Tracy and Ken long enough. It's time to see if my mind has been working on RCL for them and produced anything useful. Maybe I should go back to the beginning with them. That would be the conversation the three of us had the day we went to corporate.

Tracy said the information she had gleaned from her employees by using RCL was good, but she wasn't sure it was worth the time. The message was clear: The personal payoffs she was getting, whatever they were, were not valuable enough when compared to the time and effort it took to get the information. Thus, Tracy has a personal payoffs problem and is not really motivated to continue using RCL.

She mentioned something else that kept nagging at me. She said that getting people to talk was like pulling teeth. I instantly understand now what she was saying: In the words of Spencer, she has a perceived skill level problem and that's holding back her motivation.

Looking back on the conversation, I now see that she was telling me all I needed to know, but I wasn't attaching the proper meaning to it. This is exactly what Spencer told me on the phone when I asked him about it. When people try any new approach, they sometimes think it will be easy and suddenly discover it's harder than they anticipated. Their perception tells them they don't have the skills they need. They immediately start doubting themselves and quickly have perceived skill level problems. When this happens, they procrastinate. That's exactly what has happened to Tracy. When people struggle with something new, they often conclude that the benefits (payoffs) are not worth the effort. Again, this is precisely what has happened to Tracy. This is what she was telling me, but I was too inexperienced with RCL to understand.

What about Ken? I keep hearing his words, "I give up. I don't know what to do." It's clear now: Ken has a similar, if not bigger, perceived skill problem. How to help Ken and Tracy? I need to give that some thought.

I pull into the parking lot of the Diamond. A busy day lies ahead. I have to send corporate the RCL information, try to catch up with Cluster, and start getting ready for the monthly P & L review. I also want to start preparing for the RCL interviews. This will be a good day.

The parking lot is almost full, indicating another good night. We are making slow but steady progress. I say good morning to our night auditor and the breakfast crew and bring a pot of coffee into my office. I have a lot of work ahead of me.

I check the daily report and find we ran eighty-one percent yesterday. The Diamond has suffered along with every other hotel in Charlotte. A number of older hotels haven't made it, and we all are still struggling. With the aftermath of both the hotel recession because of over-building and the lack of real demand, we're all fighting the lack of occupancy.

The Diamond has made it through the worst part, and I have learned about the loyalties and character of people along the way. I've been truly surprised at the behavior of some people. If I had been exposed to RCL earlier, I would have known what to expect; I realize now that what I thought would motivate people simply did not. As the occupancy and profit crises developed almost overnight, people began to behave in ways I could not have imagined. My approach to understanding behavior was based on the proper recognition of the necessary elements. I had at some point in time:

1. Recognized the perceived skill level factor in some situations.
2. Worked hard at developing a reward system that was reliable and positive to most people in my organization.
3. Focused on the needs and preferences (payoffs) of others.

However, I had never thought in ways that combined all three elements to build a picture of what motivated people to behave the way they did.

I now recognize my error in missing the true motivation of others. Spencer was right when he said that unless you periodically do a Reality Check on your perceptions of people and yourself, you find yourself surprised over and over by the behavior of others. He also said that finding out what motivates people requires an understanding of payoffs that people can have. I think I will develop a list of the times I've been wrong or surprised about the way people think, feel, and behave. The summary may provide me with some insights. Alternatively, maybe I'll feel too bad about my lack of leadership skill as it relates to RCL.

The more I think about Spencer's approach, the more I realize how much my understanding of the factors that influence my behavior affects my recognition of specific factors in others. Most of what I see and hear is filtered through my perceptions of reality. Just realizing that has given me newfound hope in my ability to understand others. This whole idea may at least be the start of a new view of my life and the people in it. I am convinced that we all create our own worlds and then behave very rationally in those worlds.

With everything I have to do, I wonder if I have time to make the list. Then I realize that if it helps me now to understand Reality Check for Leaders, I'll have a lot of extra time later to do the other things I want.

With a real understanding of why people behave the way they do, I can accomplish more of my goals and objectives in less time. I begin to list the missed opportunities throughout my career. If nothing else, I can use this when I start to teach RCL. (The names have been changed to protect my bank account.)

1. Cliff Banger, the former head of the back office for the hotel. He left the moment things got tough. In fact, he handed me a projection of what he thought would happen with our cash flow and resigned three weeks later. When we began to lose business, I thought he would hang in there to the end. His idea of the end and mine were different. Using RCL, I can now see several things I missed:

   Perceived skill level. He seemed to have enough confidence in his accounting skills and not much else. I noticed his fear of public speaking even in front of small groups but never considered it to be something he couldn't overcome with practice. Wrong. He just got worse with time, and I did nothing to help him either avoid public speaking or develop the skill. I now suspect that his one and only real public appearance provided the impetus for him to find something else to do. He lost his voice and screeched out his first words. Seinfeld had a great line to describe this guy: "They say that people are more afraid of public speaking than dying. So, at a funeral they would rather be in the box than giving the eulogy." That was Cliff.

   Reward system. The reward system at the hotel was laid out for all to see. The numbers were easy enough to understand. However, I believed that autonomy was the most important reward a person could have. This belief was not shared by Cliff. When he was given the freedom to do what needed to be done, he took that flexibility and used it for his personal payoffs. Instead of improving the hotel business, he did what was needed and no more. Because I didn't keep a close eye on Cliff, his minimally acceptable behavior went unnoticed.

Payoffs. I completely missed the fact that his payoffs centered on everything other than what he was doing. His salary was in the six figures. What he did for fifteen years was provide after-the-fact information. He did not like his job. He did not find the work rewarding. In every instance where I pushed him to take a leadership role, he failed. Thinking about it now, I realize that I was asking him to go against his own perception of his skills: He did not see himself as a leader or a public speaker.

The moment he realized that his six-figure salary might be in question he implemented his plan, one he had been working on for years. He left, and we never heard from him again.

2. Milo Sanch, former head of computer services for the hotel. The Diamond is big enough to need its own computer services. We generate a daily P & L statement to keep track of all the variables that influence the hotel's bottom line. With over $1.5 million in revenue per month, we need to know what's going on and how we compare to our projections and last year's revenue. Payroll summaries, cost analyses, and occupancy projections are just some of the reports the department generates.

Perceived skill level. On the surface, Milo was a highly competent computer programmer and all around good guy. It was only after he left that I found out that most of his behavior was designed to hide the lack of confidence he had in his abilities. As it turned out, he talked a good game but had become obsolete and rigid in his behavior.

His assistant worked for years behind the scenes with never a moment's recognition. Milo treated me with deference and everyone else with open contempt. His rules for interacting and communicating were all designed to make him the source of information rather than his assistant. I missed completely his low level of self-perceived skill.

Reward system. Milo perceived the reward system of the hotel to be as rigid as he was. His only interaction was in the hallways and when a meeting was called. I believed that he, too, liked the autonomy aspect of the reward system; but I was wrong. He stayed in his position long after he stopped contributing to the hotel. The reward of autonomy was a way to hide. The fact was that he believed his good-guy, hearty-laugh, backslapping salesman approach was the key to the reward system.

Payoffs. Milo had been at the Diamond when I got there; and, given the recommendation he received from corporate, I saw no need for change. I never took the time to ask what he wanted but assumed that his idea of a payoff was similar to mine. Early in the recession, I began to hint to Milo that it was time for him to add to the profitability of the hotel. I encouraged and pressured him to behave in a way that was counter to his personal payoffs, which were not related to the technical competence of computer programming but rather involved the rewards of being the "good ol' boy." I had missed this one by a mile and in doing so cost the hotel thousands and thousands of dollars. Instead of a simple standard accounting system that would have required some revisions, Milo spent over $100,000 for an accounting system that was incredibly and unnecessarily complex. As it turns out, he made it complicated so he could protect a job that was not necessary to the hotel. His assistant, Gary, was the brains behind the department and Milo should have been terminated years ago. I promise myself I will get to know more about Gary. I will make it a point to know about his perception of his skills, the reward system, and his personal payoffs. Once again, I missed what was really important to one of my key people.

3. Wanda Bonkel, corporate office manager, fifty-eight years old, single, and a consummate professional. The VP of Operations told me this story. As we looked back, I wondered how much help Reality Check would have been to Matrix in this situation.

    Wanda was one of the most efficient office managers Matrix had. She was responsible for five bookkeepers and a receptionist, two secretaries, and numerous clerks. Without question, she always did everything asked of her and most of the time did it in the most effective possible way.

She reported to the VP of Operations. We all thought that given Wanda's history with the company and VP Long, she would be with Matrix for a very long time.

Perceived skill level. Given the almost daily praise of her performance, I have no doubt she would have scored high in skill confidence. When it came to office management, she was the best.

Reward system. Wanda knew the Matrix reward system. While we assumed she adhered to Matrix policies and procedures, the VP was wrong. As much as Wanda wanted others to follow the rules, she believed there was a separate reward system for herself. While her efficiency and expertise were unquestionable, her personal perceptions were distorted.

A key to an effective reward system is that people believe that the rewards are based on performance. In Wanda's case, she believed that the rewards were based on her right. She took advantage of the system of sick days, vacation, and other company benefits.

Payoffs. Without knowing or asking, Long assumed Wanda's payoffs were centered on a good work environment that was flexible to her personal needs when it came to time off. She thought Wanda wanted a considerate and helpful atmosphere, one where the office staff and other department managers created a pleasing work environment. Long also believed that a salary significantly above the going rate with all of the health insurance benefits and a personally designed work schedule with complete autonomy were a major portion of her payoffs. And she assumed Wanda would be as loyal to Matrix as we were to her. Wrong.

Wanda started to look for a job. While continuing her good work, she pursued every available opportunity. Then with a short, cold, and indifferent notice, she left Matrix and went to work for, of all people, Waldo Cluster.

Long couldn't have been more surprised. What she thought was the perfect match of rewards and performance turned out to be entirely misperceived.

As Long told the story about Wanda, we spent a brief time playing "ain't it awful." After just a few minutes, we laughed and agreed there was no explaining some people's behavior. On second thought, there might have been a way.

If we had had Reality Check at our disposal, we might have seen that while Wanda's confidence level was high, her perception of the reward system was distorted. Our lack of knowledge led us in the wrong direction.

Long made an assumption that because Matrix had given Wanda an inordinate amount of time off with pay when she was sick, allowed her to set her own hours, paid her above the going rate, and allowed her complete autonomy to do her job, that she would reciprocate the loyalty, compassion, and caring.

That was completely wrong. She was interested in a paycheck and health insurance, period. She went with Cluster because he promised her more money.

The real surprise to Long was that, in spite of a normally quiet demeanor, Wanda had laughed at and made fun of Cluster at every chance. When he approached her before, she told Long that she had found a way to avoid him because she would never work for a man that crude and insensitive. The truth was that, in spite of all her comments, her payoff of more money proved more dominant than any gratitude, loyalty, or concern for the people she left.

A number of people from the Matrix office tried to contact her after she left, but she ignored them all.

I now have three examples of potentially very good people lost because of our inability to see beyond our own payoffs. Further, my lack of understanding of both the perceived interest and skill levels and the hotel's implied reward system created an environment where individuals took advantage of the flexibility to pursue their own payoffs. Because I felt that autonomy was the key to a good job for me, I assumed it would be for everyone. However, Cliff and Milo misused it to pursue their personal payoffs. In Wanda's case, what was thought to be a motivating reward system was nothing of the sort. Her payoffs were centered on money, and she would do anything to insure that outcome, including going to work for Cluster.

The exercise in missed opportunities with people boosts my conviction about the value of Reality Check for Leaders. It also causes me to think of Dean, my F & B director. Have I missed something important about him? I have a great deal of confidence in him. Now I wonder if I have too much. He is great doing the behind-the-scenes work, including the planning and execution aspects of the job. Dean can wring every dime out of the food prep side of the house. His use of leftovers is creative and profitable. His control of food and labor costs is always right on target and he's not afraid to roll up his sleeves and help when the kitchen gets slammed.

I also know that the people side of the job is not his strong suit. Maybe he does not have the skills or the interest in dealing with the people aspects. That makes sense. His SISP will shed some light on that.

I know he made a poor hiring decision for the restaurant manager position. He as much as said that to me, yet he has not dealt with his problem. If the problem with Louis continues, it will become my problem and that won't be good. Maybe he has a payoff problem. Slow down, John. Go through the steps of RCL. Start with the easiest to determine and work toward the most difficult.

Handling the people part of his job may be a negative payoff for him. That may explain dragging his feet on the restaurant manager situation. Moreover, if he doesn't like that part of his job, it's a good guess that he hasn't developed the skills he needs to manage and lead people.

This is scary. How can I have been so blind? I need to think more about this. My mind is racing with ideas and plans; this is fun and exciting.

RCL is an excellent way to learn about what is motivating your people. Had I had it at my disposal five years ago, I would be a much better general manager. In fact, had I had RCL at my disposal when I was first made a department head, I could have moved up even faster.

I realize that until now I have been using the theories dealing with motivation and leadership that I was taught in college. Those, coupled with a few best selling books, comprise my storehouse of knowledge on this subject. While I still think some of those ideas are valuable, I have never before been given the structure to use what I know about people. While some of the concepts that I've been exposed to over the years have validity, they're just part of the picture of why people behave the way they do. RCL brings it all together.

The three people on my list are good examples of how wrong a leader can be. I had been surprised and sometimes hurt by their behavior. What I learned about them after they left added to my disappointment in my own abilities.

I had spent company money, time, and what I assumed was productive effort when working with each of them, to no avail. I was the one missing the signals. They were doing exactly what they needed to do in their worlds.

Although hindsight can be one hundred percent accurate, RCL could have provided me with insight in why they were thinking, feeling, and behaving the way they did. With the knowledge obtained by using RCL, I could have saved hundreds of thousands of dollars for the hotel and avoided the personal disappointment that came with failure as a leader. No more. From now on, I plan to use every RCL technique at my disposal to understand how people think, feel, and behave. Moreover, when my people do something other than what is expected, I'll have a much better understanding of why.

This has been good for me. I have a real need to learn RCL and use it in my role as a leader.

I have one other thing to do before I am completely ready to start using RCL on a daily basis. I have to do a Reality Check on myself. Without that, I will be missing the key element in understanding the perceptions of others, namely, my perception of my own world. To be a good leader, I have to know how I perceive the world. I plan to spend time getting those answers.

For now, I have to sell this to corporate. I want Matrix to benefit from the RCL approach. Personally, I want to be the RCL guru and have corporate call me to teach the approach to other GMs. I've noticed that teaching may be a payoff for me. Funny how I've ignored compliments about my public speaking ability by laughing them off. Can this be a perceived low level of skill issue? Whatever it is, this is going to be interesting and fun.

CHAPTER FIFTEEN

MAYBE MORE THAN I WANT TO KNOW ABOUT ME

A human action becomes genuinely important when it springs from the soil of a clear-sighted awareness.

Václav Havel

Before I can start on my personal ethology, I have to report to Matrix about the cost associated with bringing the RCL experience to all of our managers. In addition, I have to deal with Cluster. I should get combat pay for the time I have to spend with him and his big flunky. I know, I know, I have to remain professional, even if he acts like a complete certified idiot.

But first, Matrix. I'm a firm believer that bad news should be the first thing handled, but in this case, while I know that Cluster equals bad news, I can wait. Besides, the guy never shows up before eleven o'clock, so I have that much time anyway. I have also heard that his assistant always arrives barely thirty minutes before he does, and Cluster is none the wiser.

I call Matrix and get the VP of Operations. I ask if I may drive up to tell her about the specifics of the program. She laughs and says, "You must really want us to do this."

"I do."

"Why?"

"I think this is the best idea on understanding human behavior to come along in a long time. The concept is based on the knowledge that people's perceptions are the only reality: They create their worlds and then behave very rationally in their worlds. Moreover, all behavior that is rewarded is repeated. And that's just the beginning."

"Okay, okay, I get the idea that this is really important to you. Let's do this. We will ask Dr. Spencer to do the seminar for all our GMs and corporate people if it's not too expensive. We start with them and, if they are sold, we will move on to department managers. How much will the first one cost?"

"He is willing to lower his rate to get a foothold in the hotel industry, so he'll do it for $300 per person with a twenty-person minimum."

"Smart move on his part. If he has us as a client and we are happy, he can use that for marketing purposes. Given that, will he negotiate with us for a lower rate?"

I laugh. "You would have to know this guy to realize he won't lower his rate another dime."

"Well, I don't know if I like that or not."

I laugh again, "And he won't care."

She laughs. "He better be good with all his arrogance. Okay, let's go ahead. Why don't you work it out with the corporate schedule to see when the best time would be?"

"Thanks a lot. I really think this will help us a great deal. I'll get on it ASAP. Given your agreement there is no need for me to come up—right?"

"Right, and thank you for calling. I'll talk to you later."

"Goodbye. Wish me luck."

"Why?"

"I have to deal with Cluster today."

"Sorry. I know he's a pain. Thanks for putting up with him."

"You're welcome. I'll let you know if there's anything at all on his mind."

We laugh and hang up.

I call Cluster's office, knowing he will not be in, and leave word that I have returned his call. It will be two hours before he shows up, and I'll end up playing telephone tag with him. His idea of productivity is to show up late, have a long lunch, and then try to jam everything he has to do in a four-hour period. His people tell me that, although they are paid for an eight-hour day, he always makes them stay past five to do last minute things for him. That's enough of him for now. I'm ready to get on to my RCL work.

I must admit I'm excited about looking into the factors that influence the way I think, feel, and behave. I guess people who aren't interested in knowing more about themselves may be considered lacking self-awareness. On the other hand, they may think the whole idea of understanding anything about behavior is all a bunch of psychobabble. I'm glad. The more people competent at leading others, the more crowded it could become at the top. The old rule of thumb makes sense: Twenty percent of the people are good at what they do and are rewarded accordingly, while the rest struggle to stay even.

However, Storr is also right when he says that many people can and do lead equable and satisfying lives by basing them upon a mixture of work and more superficial relationships. Therefore, if you are one of those people, you can stop taking notes and just read the rest of this for fun. You might find it interesting to see how a really good General Manager's day is spent.

KNOWING YOU

Think about how you normally solve a people problem.

In following the Reality Check approach to understanding behavior, I first have to understand my perception of my world of work. My first step is to take the SISP, which was developed by a company that focuses on motivation and leadership research and education. I get a cup of coffee, sit at my desk, log in to the web site, and prepare to take the profile.

The comforting aspect of the SISP is that the information it reveals is available only to me unless I approve otherwise. I understand that if management companies have their employees take the profile, only aggregated information is made available to the company, not information on any individual. Hotels can, however, use the SISP as a hiring aid, as long as the respondent is aware of this purpose. This confidentiality helps ensure that employees, applicants, or students are less likely to think about the social desirability of their answers. Makes sense to me.

I call the front desk, ask the staff to hold my calls for the next hour, and begin. It's supposed to take only forty minutes to complete the profile, but I also want to have enough time to think about the results, which I will receive immediately upon completing and submitting it.

KNOWING YOU

How aware are you of your real interests and skills?

After finishing the profile, I'm fascinated by the information I have revealed about my work perceptions. According to the SISP, I really like the general manager role but am less interested in an operations position. Funny how that doesn't seem to fit my public statements about my career. If asked, I would have said my goal is to be a district manager and then an operations vice president.

Thinking about the results of the profile, I smile and say to myself, "These results suggest there may have been errors in data entry." Like most people, when confronted with a reality that does not fit my public persona, I question the instrument and not the respondent, in this case, me.

I remember taking a "strengths and weaknesses" survey in a college psychology course. The instructor said that the response from people who had actually filled out the survey and disagreed with the results was, invariably, "The strengths are accurate, but the weaknesses are overstated."

I continue reviewing the profile results and notice some areas of agreement. I'm neither skilled nor interested in hotel maintenance. I don't believe I'm skilled in the detailed actual food cost part of food & beverage but like the idea of cooking for people. On the other hand, all the bidding, vendor relationships, budgets, costing menus, and the rest are, in my mind, the tedious parts of food & beverage. Creating new dishes, plate presentations, and dining atmospheres is exciting and fun. The result is that the majority of the food & beverage position responsibilities (skills) do not hold enough rewards (interests) to offset the dislikes for me.

The SISP has helped me separate my skill and interest levels into an easily remembered chart.

RESULTS	ACTION

High Skill/High Interest------------------- Capitalize
High Skill/Low Interest-------------------- Analyze
Low Skill/High Interest------------------- Strengthen
Low Skill/Low Interest-------------------- Circumvent

The results of the profile provide me with a way to gain an understanding of the real levels of skill and interest I have in various functional areas of a hotel. Dr. Spencer says that he has become increasingly convinced that spending time on improving areas where no skill or talent exists, if there is not a deep abiding interest, is a waste of time. For me, hotel maintenance is one of those areas. I am dangerous with a screwdriver. Look out if I get my hands on a hammer. Devoting time and energy to learning the elements of an air conditioner compressor would be a waste of time. Without practice and hands-on experience, my knowledge would dissipate in a short time. Furthermore, with me, a little knowledge can be dangerous.

On the other hand, my lower-than-average interest and perceived skill level in accounting could be a detriment to my stated career aspirations. I've gotten by so far with a lot of hard work and by taking the time to understand the Matrix management system of accounting.

I can hold my own with any general manager when it comes to analyzing my departmental profits and losses, expense reports, and staffing guides. While recognized as one of the consistently accurate budget preparers, I nevertheless hate every moment of the tedious, slow, and, to me, unrewarding process known as the yearly budget. Those facts lead me to the most insightful aspect of the SISP, my results in the Operations and Leadership portions of the profile.

The most interesting, if not confusing, part of the profile results is the revelation that I may not have an interest in either a district manager or a VP of Operations position. For my generation currently working in the hospitality business, an individual's career path is clearly defined. As an employee in the hotel business, I am expected to start at a line level position and work my way up the corporate ladder.

Turnover is high in this business, a minimum of sixty-five percent per year; people with ambition can move up quickly, often too fast. My experience, as I recall with some editorial license, is that I started as a desk clerk, and within four months I was senior man in terms of longevity. I have often said that I got promoted because I was standing in the hallway when the last guy was fired.

My lack of skill combined with lack of interest made for an incredibly poor performance. I wanted a simple desk clerk job to earn money for college. The general manager, the district director, and the VP of Operations avoided asking me what I wanted to do. Their assumption was that I would be delighted with the promotions.

In reality it was troublesome because I had to learn new skills for a job I knew would not last. A short time after becoming a guest service representative, I became a:

1. Night Auditor
2. Bartender
3. Restaurant Manager
4. Food & Beverage Director
5. Assistant General Manager
6. General Manager

Each position brought more responsibility and required more hours on the job with minimal increases in income until I finally left in frustration. I bet that no one in management could have given a complete answer as to why I left the hotel.

Now when I look back, I realize that there was no reward for performance, but there was for presence. The management company filled positions with warm bodies. When people left, the reason management gave was that the former employee could not handle the pressure or that it really was a race to the door because, after all, the employee really did not have the necessary skills. No one took the time to determine the perceived skills and interests the applicant might possess.

The Delta Management Company, which operated my hotel, created a reward system centered on short-term profits. They managed by the month, and the solution to missed goals was to terminate the department head. Clearly, the reward system was based on numbers, often unrealistic, and was designed to make the owner smile for the budget meeting. After that, the company spent eleven months explaining why the budget was not met. One thing was certain: The management company did not appreciate or even understand the factors that influenced the difference between the ways people were *expected* to think, feel, and behave and the way they *actually* thought, felt, and behaved.

I feel good about Matrix. They work for both the short- and long-term goals. They're willing to expand their knowledge about human behavior as it relates to task performance. With that thought, I start on the second factor in influencing behavior, the organization's reward system.

I hear my name and look up. Tracy and Ken are standing in my doorway looking somewhat tentative, as if they want to come in and talk but are about to turn and run. I've never seen either of them acting like that.

"Can we talk?" Tracy asks.

"Sure. Come in and have a seat." I wait for them to get settled. They look at me as if I am supposed to start the meeting. I try to make them feel comfortable. "Whatever it is, it will work out fine."

They both start to talk at the same time, and Ken defers to Tracy.

"We've been going over our notes on your presentation to the management team about Reality Check for Leaders, and we realize what's going on with us." She pauses, looks at Ken, then back to me. I'm on the edge of my chair now, anxious to hear the rest of the story.

Ken takes over. "We know you're disappointed in the way we've been dragging our feet on using RCL. And we're disappointed in ourselves. We knew what we were doing. Now we know why, thanks to you and RCL."

Tracy is not one to let someone speak for her, so she jumps in. "I have a payoffs problem and a confidence problem, too."

"And I have a big confidence problem," Ken says.

I give them the biggest, warmest smile possible. "I just figured that out myself. I knew you'd get there, too. Takes a while to understand something well enough to apply it, doesn't it?"

"You can say that again," Tracy says. Ken nods in agreement.

"So what are you going to do?" I asked.

Tracy says, "We were hoping you could tell us."

"Let's look at the confidence issue first. What do you think?" I look at Tracy, then to Ken.

"I need to know more, develop my skills, find some tools that will work for me," Ken says.

"Same for me," Tracy echoes.

"Okay, let me start with you, Tracy. Sitting down and talking with your people is difficult. 'Like pulling teeth,' I believe you said. There's something different you may want to try. Instead of pushing them so hard to talk, simply *let* them talk. This way they don't feel as if you're putting them on the spot and you can relax. I know for a fact you're a great listener. If you sit back, they'll come up with the answers. Give them some notice beforehand as to what you're doing and that they will have as much time as they want to think about their payoffs, their perceptions of their skills, and how they view the reward system."

I turn to Ken. "You saw my memo about the SISP?"

"Yes."

"It's a profile that provides people in the hotel industry with a measure of their perceived skill and interest levels compared to others in the industry."

Tracy questions, "How is that going to help Ken?"

"If he gives Bob, the GSR, a chance to see how he compares to other working professionals, Bob might alter his ideas about the accepted behavior of front desk people."

Ken says, "In other words, if he finds he's not really suited for the job, he will stop being such a know-it-all."

"Right."

"What if he does have the skills and interests?"

"We'll cross that bridge... no, you'll cross that bridge when you get to it. My guess is that he's too inexperienced to have all the skills he needs."

Ken says, "It's worth a try. Anything is at this point."

I suggest, "You may want to complete the SISP yourself before giving it to him. My memo tells you how to get access to it."

"Okay, I'll do it this afternoon and then have Bob complete it tomorrow and find out what he thinks about his skills and interests."

I turn back to Tracy. "What about your payoffs problem?"

"That may not be an issue now. I see the benefits of learning more about my people, but the negative payoffs of the time and pain of doing it outweighed the positives. I think I'm over that now, especially if this listening thing really works." We all laugh, but knowing how to listen is a skill that is underrated.

"Okay, anything else?" They both shake their heads no. "All right, thanks for coming in. I feel good about where both of you are in dealing with your people and in learning how to use RCL. Let me know how things work out."

I think about the benefits I'm already receiving from RCL. Tracy and Ken have come to me with their problems already diagnosed. Not bad.

Where was I when they arrived? Oh, yes, I was wondering about the reward system for the Diamond Creek Inn and Matrix. Before I can devote time to understanding the reward system I've created at the D, I need to know about Matrix and my perception of its reward system.

The Matrix reward-for-performance system is an industry standard and clear cut. A general manager is eligible for ten percent of the positive variance in house profit—that is, the profit before taxes, depreciation, insurance, interest, and principal payments. Profit sharing is paid one-half quarterly, while the second half is held until the end of the year. Most people believe it is fair and equitable, I think.

Other management companies fool themselves into believing that their profit sharing systems are appreciated by all. The fact is that I know a few general managers who brag that they can "work" the system to take advantage of the profit sharing plan. They simply withhold needed expenditures to improve their profit pictures for the short run. One particularly egregious example I knew about years ago involved a frightened and bitter older GM who particularly offended his employees, coworkers, and the staff at his management company. To increase his personal monetary payoff, he consciously deferred important expenditures. The joke was that if he could not get it capitalized, the hotel would not get the item—no way. He got away with it for awhile, and the hotel suffered because of his unscrupulous behavior. His employees feared and despised him, but the management company he worked for only looked at the numbers. As a result, he stayed. The employees that left his hotel tried to tell the management company, but no one would listen. This company had created a reward system that focused on personal monetary gains at the expense of the hotel. The result was that an unprincipled person was rewarded by a flawed system, with unintended negative consequences.

As far as I'm concerned, the monetary aspects of the Matrix reward system are fundamentally sound and fair. I have the opportunity to negotiate my yearly budget as well as all departmental profit numbers. Expenses and capital items are discussed, and I never feel that I'm being imposed upon. The final budgets are fair and realistic. I'm given a challenge but not an insurmountable one; I believe that I can perform every quarter, all things being equal. Moreover, when I do perform, I share fairly in the profits as outlined in the plan.

My salary increases are a function of rises in costs of living and performance evaluations conducted by the staff at Matrix. Seldom do I object to my evaluations, although there have been times when I thought the staff had GM favorites that they let slide in terms of performance. Because everyone knows everything about the evaluations, general managers compare percentage increases. Some of the Matrix group accountants are like giant sieves when it comes to keeping information confidential. One or two of them live for gossip.

In fact, I think that part of their reward system is talking about people who actually have a life. They play "ain't it awful" daily—it seems to be a valued payoff for them. Quick to judge, they walk around in a self-righteous stupor, ignoring their dull lives by focusing on the lives of others.

In any event, we all know within a day or so what the percentage increases are for each general manager. As far as I can tell from the lack of turnover, the majority of GMs are happy with the system. I decide to make a list of what I think are the other elements of the Matrix reward system.

YOU SHOULD KNOW

The perceived reward system is an organization's most effective training program.

If monetary reward is one element, what else makes up the reward system that Matrix has established? I decide to call and ask the VP of Operations. She answers on the second ring.

"I'm working on the RCL material and wonder if you have a list of what Matrix considers to be the elements that comprise its reward system," I tell her.

"Say what!?" she replies and laughs.

"You know, the things the company does to reward, or for that matter punish, people for their task behavior."

"I've never thought about that. It sounds as if it could be a very important list to have everyone understand."

"I think it could be extremely important in understanding why people behave the way they do."

"Tell me more."

I laugh. "Well, that's why I called you. I need help in determining what makes up the reward system."

"That's funny. We both know that this reward system is important but haven't taken the time to determine what is in it. I guess all organizations have a perceived reward system, even if they don't acknowledge its presence. We should find out about ours, don't you think?"

"Absolutely. I believe that a reward system is the best training program an organization has."

After a long pause, she continues, "You know, John, you can sound like a college professor sometimes. Keep talking."

"Well, how people perceive they are rewarded or punished for their behavior, by the written and unwritten rules in an organization, is the most effective training program the organization has because it determines how people will behave.

"The written policy and procedures are clear cut enough. The unwritten responses to behavior make up the 'stealth' reward system. Although a good company reviews the written reward system on a regular basis, there is no mechanism for determining and reviewing the informal, unwritten, and sometimes hidden elements of the system."

"Enough, enough! You've given me way too much to think about. Is this some of Spencer's thinking?"

"No, actually, it's mine. He says rewarded behavior is repeated. I thought of the training program aspects of the reward system."

"Well, good for you. I bet your Dr. Spencer will be interested in your theory. I have a staff meeting in a few minutes that I need to get ready for, so I have to go. Let's meet and talk about the Matrix reward system. Should I invite anyone else?"

"It's up to you, but I think anyone at any level willing to be candid could be helpful."

"Okay, let me think about who and we'll call and set up a time good for you."

Now, there is a reward system element. She is pursuing my idea and will work around my schedule. It feels good to be noticed and appreciated.

"Great. Just let me know. Bye."

YOU SHOULD KNOW

Effective leaders know and review both the formal and informal reward systems and their impacts on employee behavior.

223

When I look at the clock it is 12:30 p.m. I call Cluster's office again and get the answer I was expecting: He has gone to lunch.

I go to the dining room and see Tracy with some potential clients. She motions for me to come over and introduces me to her two guests. She asks if I want to join them. I say something about a budget meeting, thank them for considering the Diamond, and go to the kitchen. Sammy, the lunch chef, makes me a ham and cheese on sourdough. I grab a diet Pepsi and go back to my office.

I turn on the news and eat my lunch. As usual, there is not much good happening in the world. After fifteen minutes, the no-news stories come on. That's where newsreaders fill in the time with breaking news about how nothing has changed. I switch to TCM. Good, old movies with good acting and great stars are nice to have in the background and aren't depressing.

I'm finishing my lunch when Dean walks into my office. He looks unhappy.

"Come in," I say. "Have a seat."

He flops down in a chair and stares at me for several seconds before saying anything. I wait. He takes a deep breath. "I took the SISP a little while ago." He stops. I wait again. "It pegged me. I've known for a long time, but I never wanted to admit it."

I can see that his mind is racing, although where, I do not know. I can make a guess. Judging by the discouragement and disappointment on his face, his SISP results probably show he is not well suited for his job as F & B Director.

He sits there in silence. One of the things I learned long ago is to let people talk. If I say much here, I can shut him down. He wants me to listen. If he wants me to talk, he'll let me know.

"My skills and interests are high on the technical part of my job. The problem is that I don't have the leadership skills I need. Worse yet, I don't really have an interest in being a manager and leader. Funny, isn't it? All these years and I've gotten by pretty well. What do you think of that, John?"

I know what he means. At least, I think I do. "So how have you managed all these years?" I turn the question back to him.

"Simple really. I've been lucky, I guess. I've always hired good people. They have the skills and interest, and they like independence. All I have to do is point them in the right direction and stay out of their way. The problem is making a bad hire, as I did with our restaurant manager, and I have a problem on my hands. I'm not good at fixing people problems. I don't have the patience to coach and develop him; and because of that, I don't think it's fair to just boot him out." He pauses for a long time before speaking again. "What do you think?"

"Have you considered doing a Reality Check on yourself? See if that will help you think through things more clearly."

"You really think that will help?"

"I'm positive it will." I stop to let him think about that. "Have you considered having your restaurant manager take the SISP?"

"What good would that do?" He sits in silence, wheels turning.

Finally, I say, "Well, it might help him see he's not cut out for the job."

"He knows he's not. The SISP could be just what he needs to clarify what he already knows. Just like me. Well, I talked myself into that, didn't I?"

For the first time, a ray of hope crosses his face. "I'll start working on that right now." He gets up and walks toward the door, stops, and turns around. "Thanks for listening." He leaves looking more hopeful than when he walked into the office.

I'm not sure where all of this will lead, but I'm willing to continue working with Dean using RCL and seeing what happens. I'm reminded of Dr. Spencer. He said, "One of the most important things you can do as a leader is get people in the right jobs." I believe that is about to happen here with a couple of people.

It's around one thirty, so I call Cluster again and get the same answer—still out for lunch. I ask the receptionist if he really has an office there and she laughs. She promises to have him call me when he gets back, if he does. I now want to get to him before he starts bothering people at Matrix, but there is nothing I can do until he calls me back.

I call Stan, the general manger of the Hampton, and ask him what Cluster may want with me. Stan says he doesn't know but that the guy likes to play "gotcha" management. It could be anything from another dumb idea to some perceived slight on the part of the staff at the Hampton. Now, there is another example of an unwritten reward system. This guy has convinced his employees that he hides in the background and second guesses their decisions, so they are rewarded for doing just the minimum and no more.

"Other than Cluster, how are things going?" I ask.

"Great. If the guy would just go away again, we would all be happier here."

I laugh. "Now there's a reward system element."

Stan says, "A what?"

"Never mind. I'll tell you about it later. If you think of anything he may want, give me a heads up."

"I will. And, by the way, the numbers look good, and as long as Cluster stays away, my people are happy."

"I know, Stan. Hang in there."

Does Cluster know how dysfunctional he is? Has anyone told him? No, probably not. I'm not going to be the one, but someone should.

I hate to start my list of reward system elements and be interrupted by Cluster, so I work on the monthly P & L statement for a while. I already know that my strong suit is not accounting, but Matrix has a great on-the-job program in budget preparation and analysis of profit and loss statements. Because there is not a single accounting method every management company uses, it's often difficult to adjust to a new company's system.

Matrix has a sound educational approach to budgeting and P & L analysis—an approach that provides new hires with a sense of confidence (skill level) and more long-term employees with a feeling of security (reward system). The trainee is paired with a general manager who has considerable experience and helps the employee through two or three P & L statements. After that, the employee is expected to attend P & L meetings, alone or with his or her department heads, if desired.

I work on the P & L until three thirty and then leave to work out. By the time I get back, it's close to five o'clock, and still no word from Cluster.

As I call Cluster's office for the third time today, Tracy comes in and asks if she can stay. I say yes and wait for the phone at Cluster's office to be answered. The receptionist says she gave him the message but that he isn't in the office at the moment. I ask her to leave another message to let him know I tried again. How urgent is his concern if he doesn't bother to call back?

Stan has told me that he does that all the time: Big panic and then nothing. The more he cries wolf, the less people pay attention. Some day that will really cost him.

I turn to Tracy, "What's up?"

She smiles. "It's just amazing how easy it is to get information about people directly from them. I have always struggled when I tried to get people to talk about themselves. What I've learned is that I push too much and make them uncomfortable. Just asking and being quiet works very well. And it's not just listening, it's centered listening. I read about it in *Reality Check*. It's when you focus on the real meaning of what people are saying rather than just the words."

"Sounds a little like psychobabble to me."

"No, it's just a better focus on what people are really trying to tell you. Do you remember when I tried to tell you that I was uncomfortable about using RCL, and it took you a while to understand my concerns?"

"Oh, yeah."

"Okay, with centered listening you would have picked up my lack of confidence more quickly. It's not the only way; it's just a more effective and more efficient way to understand what people are saying. And I bet all it takes is practice because the more I use it, the more I hear."

"Good for you, and thanks for learning about RCL."

"You're welcome. See you at the GM Reception."

"Your turn?"

"Yes, and right after, I'm going home to relax."

When she leaves, I spend about an hour finishing my work on the P & L, shut down the office for the day, and head to the General Manager's Reception. We should change the name of this thing to, I don't know, the "Thank You Reception" or the "We Appreciate You Reception" or something other than GM. Then I could start taking turns coming to these things.

CHAPTER SIXTEEN

AN ORGANIZATION'S REWARD SYSTEM

Perfection of means and confusion of goals seem, in my opinion, to characterize our age.

Albert Einstein

I head to the reception. This day has gone by quickly. Did I really accomplish anything or was it a series of false starts and delays? Sometimes I wonder how productive I really am. And although I think I'm more productive than most, days like today make me doubt this assumption. Tomorrow will be better.

I walk into the reception and smile when I see Ken and Tracy handling the crowd. There must be fifty or sixty people, and most seem to be enjoying themselves. I make the rounds, say hello to our regulars, and introduce myself to the new people. One fear I have at these events is introducing myself to someone who has been staying with us for a while. I do well tonight, and by six thirty almost everyone is gone. We have a few people trying to make their dinner out of the hors d'oeuvre buffet we put out. At an ADR of $211, they are certainly entitled.

As I finish a conversation with one of our long-time guests it occurs to me that Dean was not here. In fact, he seldom comes to the GM Receptions. I don't require it of all our managers, but they know I want them here, at least to make a brief appearance.

KNOWING YOU

Reality comes when people become aware they are denying or ignoring the truth about individuals or situations.

Come to think of it, it's been weeks since Dean has been here. Rewarded behavior is repeated. That means he's being rewarded for not showing up. He's not the people-oriented type, so he doesn't like this kind of function. His payoff stems from avoiding these receptions; attending produces a negative payoff for him.

Now that I think about it, Dean rarely socializes, although he's pleasant when around people. He definitely prefers to bury himself in work he can do alone. For example, he loves all of the numbers and cost control activities.

All of this matches what he recently told me. He likes to hire competent, independent managers and let them do their job. In other words, he doesn't have to deal with many people issues. It's going to be interesting to see what he comes up with when he does a Reality Check on himself.

As the last of our guests leave, a GSR walks up and hands me a message from Cluster. He evidently waited until six thirty to call looking for me. When the desk told him I had left for the day, he went nuts; insulted the GSR, the hotel, and me; and hung up. Cluster is about five feet, five inches, weighs about 190 pounds, and as far as I can tell, is as soft as the Pillsbury doughboy but, evidently, very aggressive on the telephone.

I ask Donna if she's all right and she laughs and says, "No problem. Little Hitler gives us a good laugh every time he calls." I laugh and thank her for putting up with the jerk. I say goodbye to Tracy and Ken and head to the kitchen to get something to take home. Ralph, the night kitchen manager, tries to talk me into a steak or some pork chops, but I tell him I still haven't cooked the last steak he gave me. We settle on a tuna sandwich, some pickles, and a piece of lemon pie.

I still have Dean on my mind, so I walk by the restaurant out of curiosity. I don't expect to see him there. I am looking for the restaurant manager. Standing and watching from a distance, I see Louis towering above one of the shortest, sweetest women I have ever known and one of the best servers ever to work at the D.

The body language indicates he is upset with her and that she's taking it but not liking a word of what he's saying to her. It's a short exchange and, when he finishes, he points in the direction of a table with six people. She turns immediately and marches in that direction. He watches her for a couple of minutes, then turns away, talking to himself and throwing his hands up in the air with "I give up" written all over him.

I can hear Spencer's voice: "If somebody is performing poorly, someone is letting them get by with it." That someone is Dean. Worse yet, I've been letting Dean get by with not dealing with what is an obvious problem. Well, that will end first thing tomorrow.

I drive home, change, and watch a show on Fox News Network I recorded earlier. Brit Hume and his "panel of experts" present the news in a way that is not too heavy. While slightly to the right of center, it does have one of my favorite NPR people, Mara Liaison. A bright and well-spoken woman who can hold her own with anyone, she provides a healthy balance to my perception of world events. The other thing I like about the news is that Hume does not take himself too seriously, although it is fun to watch him turn into a lawyer when there is a need. The result is that I get the news without too much selling on either the right or the left. I can only take an hour of television and radio news a day. The other way I keep up is to read *Time* for the left-leaning perspective and *National Review* for the right.

After dinner, I decide to work on the reward system idea. I go to my study, turn on my desktop computer, put some Georgia fatwood in the fireplace, and start a small fire.

I bring up www.DirectionsForHospitality.com, click on the *Schilagi Organization Survey* (SOS), and review the potential summary of results. The SOS, which is currently in the beta testing stage, will operate on the premise that the best way to determine the perceived reward system in any organization is to ask people in a non-threatening way.

It will present a series of statements and ask people to respond according to the following scale:

Strongly agree	=5
Agree	=4
Uncertain	=3
Disagree	=2
Strongly disagree	=1

I can take the beta survey and have the results in a matter of minutes. Matrix could really use this approach to understand their reward system. Employees will be able to take the SOS, and Matrix could review summary results and get a clear picture of how its reward system is perceived. It looks like it will be a wonderful instrument for strengthening good companies.

Matrix's written policy is easy enough to find, while the unwritten reward system is more difficult to discern. I wonder how many organizations actually know the image they present to their employees.

However, organizations don't create the informal reward systems; people who represent the organization do. Employees may say, "I hate the company I work for," when what they really mean is "I hate the person I work for in this company." There are no exceptions. The supervisor at any level is the primary reward system at any level. I say "primary" because some aspects of the reward system are not totally in the hands of the supervisor. For example, higher-level management dictates bonuses, plays a heavy hand sometimes in promotions, and establishes guidelines about giving pay raises. Nevertheless, the people supervising, managing, and leading others are, for the most part, the ones handing out payoffs, both positive and negative.

SOMETHING TO THINK ABOUT

How is it possible that a single person can be the primary reward system of an organization?

The idea of the manager as the conveyor of the reward system is both fascinating and frightening. Any company that wants to succeed must have standardized written policies and procedures. The written policies represent the intended reward system of the organization.

The way a supervisor or manager implements the policies determines how those policies are perceived. When people talk about a great company to work for, they're talking about the great leaders they experience. Conversely, when people say they hate a company, their perceptions are based primarily on their experiences with their managers or supervisors.

To carry that one step further, organizations do not have goals; people have goals, or really payoffs, that color the picture of their worlds of work and their lives. How many times have you heard leaders say, "This organization stands for_____," when what they really mean is "I stand for_____." What matters isn't what these people say but the way they think and behave. Their behavior determines the employees' perception of the reward system. I've met leaders who talk a good game, but when the time comes for them to perform, they're "all hat, no cattle."

I'm anxious to meet with the Matrix people and find out what they consider to be the real reward system. I wonder if they will really know. We'll see.

The idea that manager behavior determines the reward system now seems so logical that the thought of bringing it up is embarrassing. It is like walking into a dark room and announcing that the light could be turned on. Everyone would know that there is light available, but not all would act on that knowledge.

Wow, it is almost one o'clock. Better get some sleep.

I sleep until seven o'clock and get to the hotel around eight. That tuna sandwich for dinner wasn't enough, and I'm hungry. I go to the front desk and am annoyed to find a pile of newspapers on the counter. I ask Cindy to move the papers behind the desk and to hand them to people who ask.

She looks puzzled.

"Cindy, do you know why I want you to hand the newspapers to our guests?"

"No, sir. I thought maybe it was because you didn't like things piled up on the top of the counter."

"No, it's because when the customer walks up and picks up a paper on his own, he doesn't connect getting the paper with our giving it to him."

She looks at me as if I'm nuts but says, "Oh, I understand."

"When they ask for a paper and then say thank you, the gift we are giving them registers."

She laughs. "Oh, now I really understand."

"Good and thanks for helping with that."

What I want to tell her is that handing customers a newspaper is giving them a payoff. I wonder how differently the staff would behave if they remembered that people pursue personal payoffs. The more payoffs we give, the more our customers will like us and the more business we will do. Then there will be more payoffs for everybody who works here. It all seems so simple—now.

FOCUS ON YOU

Does understanding that people pursue personal payoffs affect your behavior and decisions?

I go to the restaurant and order breakfast. What I want is two scrambled eggs and some Belgian waffles. What I order is two scrambled eggs, bacon, and toast. I do not order grits, one of my favorite foods in the morning. I am working on getting to 190 pounds again. Just as I thank Madge, my server, for the pot of coffee, Tracy walks in and asks if I mind some company.

Let's see. Have breakfast sitting across from this stunningly beautiful and intelligent woman, or read this newspaper with headlines announcing more death in the Middle East, oil prices at their highest in ten years, and another member of Congress indicted on bribery charges? I say, "Have a seat."

When Madge returns, Tracy orders. I notice that she looks up and smiles at Madge. That reminds me of how often people in restaurants or bars ignore the persons waiting on them. The job of servers is hard enough without the added insult of being discounted. Tracy has style along with her other attributes.

"So, Tracy, what's going on with your life these days?"

"Not much. I love my work, or most of it. I have almost finished decorating my home. I'm looking for a new car, and my social life is, you know, yada, yada, yada."

We both burst out laughing at the *Seinfeld* reference and I play along with the scene. "But you skipped over the best part."

She follows through just as Elaine does. "No, I told you about the decorating." She laughs. "You're getting good at the *Seinfeld* references. For a guy who never watched the original episodes, you certainly have picked up on the reruns. So, any advice on a car?"

"Sure, it's easy. Buy the car that makes you smile."

"What?"

"Are you a driver or commuter? The first enjoys getting there; the commuter just wants to get there in whatever is available."

"Then I'm a commuter."

"Oh, so what have you seen?"

We talk cars until the food arrives, and Madge says "Eggs, bacon, no grits," and I say to them, "Have I ever told you my story about grits?"

"No."

"Well, I left home when I was seventeen to see the world, or at least the United States. I had hitchhiked for a day or so and early one morning I found myself in Alabama. I walked to a little rustic roadside diner and ordered bacon, eggs, and coffee. In those days you got toast and, what I found out later were grits, as part of the breakfast. Anyway, when the waitress—back then it was waitress—put down the plate, I saw this white mass of something on the dish and I said in my clearest New York accent, 'Yo, what's that on my dish?'

"She came back, looked at the dish and said, 'Where?'

"I pointed to the white things and said, 'There.'

"She laughed and said, 'Them is grits,' and when she did, two guys at the counter laughed, too.

"I said, 'Fuggedaboutit, it's eating my eggs.' At this point everyone was laughing, and she took the plate back and put my eggs and bacon on another dish. They asked where I was from, and we talked all through breakfast. It was a fun time."

Tracy was still laughing when she said, "Do you still not eat grits?"

"As it turns out, a few years later I tried them with butter, salt and pepper and they have become one of my favorite things with breakfast."

We talk while we eat. As always, she is a good listener and can hold her own on the subjects we discuss. I ask, "Tracy, what do you think about the reward system we have in this hotel?"

"I'm not sure I know what you mean by reward system," she says.

"Well, I think of the reward system as those written and unwritten polices, rules, whatever, about the positive and negative things you receive as part of your job."

"Like salary and benefits?" she questions.

"Maybe I can show you. Sit here while I get something copied."

I go to the front desk and have them make two copies of my summary results from the SOS. I give a copy to Tracy and ask her to read and review the responses and get back to me. I don't ask her to take the SOS yet. We finish our breakfast time by talking about new business for the hotel.

It is almost nine o'clock when we go back to our offices. Tracy thanks me. "My pleasure," I say. "Have a good day and let me know what you think of that list."

I'm wondering if she's gone to the website yet to take a look at the SISP. But it was only yesterday that I gave her the information. Was it only yesterday? I can't even remember. So much is going on that everything seems like a blur. Anyway, I'm sure she'll get to it soon.

I walk through the kitchen to the laundry room, then through the banquet setup areas and the entire first floor of the hotel. I make sure that I say hello to everyone on staff at least every two weeks. I have a sheet to help me remember where I visit each day. Some places I see during the natural course of a day—like the front desk, restaurant, and kitchen—while other departments and people I have to go find. The hotel is so big that it's difficult to catch everyone at every shift. I make it my personal goal to keep up with the most important resource a hotel has—its people.

I get back to my office around ten o'clock and am pleasantly surprised. There are no messages lying on my desk. Before getting too excited, I check my voicemails and, when there are none, I start on emails. Today is going to be good, a nice message-, voice-, and email-free Friday.

When I left the GM Reception last night, I promised myself to deal with Dean today. I've been negligent on the restaurant situation long enough.

Before I can get my mind in gear, Dean bursts into my office, wide smile across his face, visibly very pleased with himself, and sits down waving some papers in his hands.

I laugh. "Have a seat."

He laughs out loud, a rarity for him. "I had my restaurant manager take the SISP. And we are on our way to solving the problem. Well, half way."

I smile and nod. "Go on."

"He just left my office. Said his SISP results showed he has neither the skill nor interest to be a good restaurant manager. In addition, his skill and interest on the leadership side were also low. He said he knew all that, but the SISP helped him accept it. His plan is to stay here until I get a replacement, then he'll move on and try to figure out what he wants to do with his life. He's still young."

"So, the problem is half over."

"Right, I'll start the wheels turning today to find a replacement."

I raise my eyebrows and give a facial expression that I hope conveys what I'm thinking. Apparently, it does.

"Okay, okay, hiring the right person will be my first priority. I'll for sure be using the SISP."

I smile, again reflecting on all that is happening. Everybody says people hate change. I say people resist going somewhere they haven't been before until they see the payoffs that are waiting for them. Most times, you have to nudge people before they know for certain the payoffs are real. Dean now knows the payoffs that come from using the SISP indeed are real, and I feel that he will use the profile when he needs accurate information on the interest and skill levels of his people.

I look over my list of tasks for the week and find that the only thing I have not done is have the discussion with Cluster. The notes alongside the task indicate that I've certainly tried to get in touch with him. Because Cluster is such a jerk, I decide to cover myself and send an email to Dana Long about my numerous calls and the results. She replies, "I will use this if he calls me. Keep trying. Thanks." I call his office again and leave my fourth message with the receptionist.

It is interesting how Cluster has established a negative reward system in which people must take time to be sure he doesn't hurt their careers. The time spent in thinking about what he may do next could instead be used in helping his business grow and prosper. Instead, people who work with him spend their time either staying away or being sure he doesn't play "gotcha" management. Thank goodness he has a weak mind. When you have a battle of wits with this guy, you can check your brains at the door.

Do company and organization leaders know when they create a negative reward? How are negative rewards created? How can someone identify a negative reward? Is the phrase, "negative reward," an oxymoron? Should I be using the word "payoff" rather than "reward"? Does it make sense to say that the organization creates the reward system and the individual creates the payoffs? Or that when organizations and companies have negative rewards, people perceive negative payoffs? I believe that people work just as hard, if not harder, to avoid a negative reward or payoff. So, if the environment includes negative payoffs, the effort of the employees is directed to avoidance of those negatives. My good buddy, Mr. Cluster, offers some great examples of negative payoffs: making harsh verbal reprimands, calling people names, making threats. And some of his more subtle but equally negative payoffs include making facial expressions of displeasure, eye-rolling, and giving someone the silent treatment.

People behave in ways to avoid receiving negative payoffs—that is, they are motivated to meet expectations because they want to avoid receiving a negative payoff. Many managers use this as their motivation strategy. It produces results—but only in the short run. People soon tire of working hard to avoid the negative. Many leave for other jobs. Others stay, but they rebel; they work against the manager to get him back.

Giving negative payoffs destroys relationships and in the long run causes individual and organizational performance to plummet. Cluster's way of dispensing negative payoffs is a prime example of the impact it can have on business success.

YOU SHOULD KNOW

Withholding payoffs runs counter to the idea that people pursue personal payoffs.

Withholding positive payoffs also is very damaging. I know a general manager, named Benny something-or-other, who believes that real leaders do not have to say thank you. Benny is so uncaring that he has created an environment in his hotel that treats the guest as an unavoidable pain. As a result, his guest relations scores are the lowest in the district, and he never understands why. The answer may lie in the way he establishes the reward system.

His loyalty and integrity can be bought for a dollar and some change. The employees know this and that their loyalty is worth nothing. Turnover in his hotel is over 120% a year, and again, he never knows why. His excuse for the problem is that the management company he works for doesn't offer enough benefits. I know the benefits offered by his company are, in fact, very competitive.

I also know that people start looking for other jobs as soon as they have to deal with him. Some line people don't leave, but that's because he doesn't interact with them. Most competent managers leave after a short time, while the losers stay on longer.

I know of one sales and marketing director who worked for him, and after five years of less than average performance, just walked out and took whatever business he could with him. The reward system created by Benny is one of no loyalty and no ethics; and the sales director acted rationally in the world that had been created. After he resigned and told Benny why, Benny's first response was to offer him a raise to stay. It turns out that Benny's answer to everything is more money.

That is a great example of someone falsely assuming that a payoff important to him works for everyone. Money can only hold some people in a bad environment for so long. Even then, they are constantly looking for ways out. What kind of performance do you get from people who are looking every day for better places to work? Even the lazy and incompetent ones leave when offered better jobs. A work world where you never hear "thank you" or "good job" or where a steady diet of criticism is dished out every day has to be a miserable place.

In another example, one of Benny's front desk managers came in to cover for a sick night auditor. He worked all night and balanced the next morning. This is considered by most as going beyond the call of duty. Benny didn't thank him or even suggest that the guy go home to get some sleep. I heard this story from Ken when he applied for the front desk manager position with me.

My thoughts on reward systems have been racing and rambling around. I need to get them organized and find some closure on this.

First, there is the organizational reward system; it consists of compensation (profit sharing, bonuses, pay) and benefits (health and life insurance, tuition reimbursement plans, training and career development programs, etc.).

Second, there is the reward system that centers on the way supervisors, managers, and leaders treat their employees—the individuals on their team. I'm going to start calling this "the leader's reward system." It consists of all the things leaders say and do with their people, such as giving or withholding praise, saying thank you or not, and providing coaching when it is needed rather than leaving people on their own to learn. These are just a few examples, obviously.

FOCUS ON YOU

As a leader, do you have a clearly defined reward system?

People have probably never heard of this distinction between organization and leader reward systems. But I know the distinction exists, and I think it's good to give the systems names. I know this certainly broadens the traditional view of a reward system, but it's very consistent with the three elements of Reality Check for Leaders: Perceived skills drive results, rewarded behavior gets repeated, and people pursue personal payoffs.

Since I have some time, I decide to put together my plan for next week. I found out years ago that cleaning my desk every Friday and making a list of things I have to do the following week gives me a wonderful sense of structure for the weekend or whenever I have time off. Walking into my office to a clean desk every day gives me a sense of order. Moreover, the list helps me keep work issues off my mind when I'm away.

This is a little secret I've used for years to keep my work world in order. I've watched people walk into cluttered offices every day and spend the first hour trying to get organized. Usually they have a filing system that consists of piling things up in stacks without regard for structure or process. The result is a complete lack of organization, accompanied by an almost comical devotion to the idea that they can find whatever they need.

When I interact with the clutter bugs, I always keep my own copies and never give them originals of anything. I also always plan to remind them of what they've promised to do. Otherwise, the promised work often never gets done. Over time, I also notice that these same people wait until the last minute to complete their promised assignments and are, more often than not, late. The universal response to waiting until the last minute is, "I work better under pressure." As a rule, and psychologically speaking, that is nonsense. Okay, I will concede that some people do work better under pressure; but for most, I find it's just a good way to rationalize procrastination.

The payoff for clearing my desk every day and making a list once a week is a sense of closure. I add to the list of things to do during the week, but on weekends I know I don't have to think about work for a while, a nice feeling that is well worth the effort. That's a big payoff for me, but I realize it may not be for everyone.

On the other hand, this could happen: A really, really top executive in Washington, D.C., walked by a subordinate's office at the end of a day and said, "I hope your mind is not as cluttered as your desk." The subordinate vowed to keep his desk clean, and every day before leaving he filed papers and cleaned off his desk. He got in the habit of having his desk cleared of everything other than what he was working on at the time. One day the same executive walked by and said, "I hope you are working on more than what's on your desk."

Ah, the reward system.

CHAPTER SEVENTEEN

REALITY CHECK IN ACTION

Greed is a bottomless pit which exhausts the person in an endless effort to satisfy the need without ever reaching satisfaction.

Erich Fromm

My recent experiences with Ken and Tracy have revealed that RCL can work in most situations. However, when people are one-dimensional in their payoffs, the task may become more difficult. I wonder, for example: When greed is someone's major payoff, why can't I use the elements in RCL to work with that person, however distasteful? While the vast majority of people don't abide by that single payoff because they need more in their lives than just money, some people are motivated primarily by the accumulation of money and things at any cost. If the motivating factor is always money, can't I focus all discussions and actions on that one aspect? The answer is, yes.

Ken represents a person with a variety of payoffs. He knows the reward system at the Diamond, and it fits with his personal payoffs. When I work with him, the factors that influence his behavior at work are readily apparent. When I try to work with Waldo Cluster, his payoffs are also obvious: They are greed combined with looking important to others. Each man has created his world and behaves rationally in that world.

So far, so good. Dealing with people like Ken or Cluster is a matter of understanding the factors influencing their behaviors. I've had success with Ken but not yet with Cluster. However, now I know that focusing on his two major needs will make him controllable. He has, after all, only inherited money; he has no real influence. If he can be controlled, then the need to be as far away from him as possible will diminish. If you have to lead up, you lead up.

But what about cutting your losses as an option? Too often I have seen managers put up with individuals that just do not fit. Dean putting up with Louis is a good example. Actually, I, too, have made excuses for people who need to be gone. What's the payoff in that for me? Is my indecision an attempt to force my hiring decision to work? I know that it's easier for me to terminate people I did not hire. If I made the hiring decision (or agreed with a manager about hiring someone), I have more of an investment in that decision working out.

Now, with RCL, I'll be able to understand why certain people don't fit in particular jobs, and I'll have a rational reason for terminating the relationship if I have to. RCL also helps me realize that every day a non-fit individual stays on the job is a daily reinforcement of the negative perception of the organization's reward system. When other people in the organization see individuals that just don't belong, they begin to question the standards of the company. If the organization's stated objective is quality performance, and leaders allow minimally acceptable behavior to persist, soon everyone questions the quality standard.

For this to make sense, I need a definition of non-fit persons and their impact on the organization. I also understand that the Diamond Creek Inn day-to-day reward system is primarily up to me. If people are working for more than just money, it's up to me to understand what I'm offering vis-à-vis their personal payoffs.

For me to identify non-fit individuals (NFIs), I need to know the answers to the following questions:

1. What are their perceived skill levels for the positions or tasks? Individuals who start tasks believing they are not qualified have a strike against them. Conversely, individuals who are overly confident about their skills are also suspect. Remember the "rarely right, but never in doubt" guy? Most adults, when asked, believe they can jump rope for three minutes without error. Not only are they wrong, but— and this I find fascinating—the vast majority have not even tried to jump rope in years. Knowing individuals' perceptions of their skill levels will add important pieces to the puzzle of why they behave the way they do.

2. What are their perceived interest levels? How many people are bored with their jobs? People who go to work every day thinking they hate this work or who don't know if they can do this again tomorrow are individuals that will exhibit, at best, minimally acceptable behavior. People who find their work exciting and interesting, on the other hand, will be willing participants in most assigned tasks.

3. What is their understanding of, and confidence in, the organizational reward system? If they have high degrees of both understanding and confidence in the reward system of the organization, then I can be assured that they will try their best to accomplish the objectives at hand.

    If, however, they do not have confidence that the reward system will function the way they perceive it should, then they will be less willing to perform. It is vital for a leader to understand that the organization's and leader's reward systems are the best training programs available.

4. What are their personal payoffs? Knowing the personal payoffs of the people I work with is the last element of information I need to complete the picture. Personal payoffs are as varied as the people who have them, and knowing them will help me understand why individuals behave the way they do. I now have a better understanding about the value of payoffs. Clearly, the organization's reward system, represented and implemented primarily by the leader, must complement the payoffs that people want. Rewards that do not reflect the personal payoffs of the individual do not contribute to the continued performance of that person.

So, if I want to understand why individuals are behaving the way they are, I need to get the answers to these questions.

The SISP will get me the answers to the first two questions. The SOS will get me the answer to the third question. The personal payoffs (question 4) can be discovered by centered listening.

YOU SHOULD KNOW

The best answers come from a willingness to communicate with your people. Profiles, surveys, and tests can make it easier but are not infallible solutions.

The personal payoffs of an individual can be the most challenging of the four elements. As simple as it may seem to sit down and ask individuals what is important in their lives, the answers can be elusive. The idea that you shouldn't discuss religion or politics implies there are some areas of human behavior best left alone. I understand that asking individuals about their personal goals and aspirations carries with it three major hurdles that have to be overcome before progress can be made.

First, I have to have the trust of the employee that everything said in the discussion about personal payoffs will be held in confidence. I've met managers who are considered the village voice when it comes to gossip and rumors. Clearly, this type of manager or employee cannot be trusted with real information about the person being questioned. If I have the reputation as a gossip or a talker, I may as well not bother trying to gain real information from others about their personal payoffs.

Second, my people must understand that a discussion of personal payoffs does not involve judgment on my part. Remember, their payoffs are not good or bad; they are just payoffs. If I am known as the judgmental type, the answers I get will be what psychologists call "socially desirable." Socially desirable answers are ones in which respondents answer the way they think you want them to answer. The responses, if taken seriously, can lead in the wrong direction.

Third, I have to think of the payoffs described by my people in terms of what the organization's reward system can do to help them achieve their personal payoffs. The reality is that if the organization's reward system doesn't accommodate the personal payoffs of individuals, performance will suffer. The reward system can be neutral relative to obtaining a personal payoff, but it cannot be negative if it is to be effective.

Similarly, individuals' personal payoffs cannot be too disconnected from what is needed by the organization. I have to view individual payoffs in light of how they fit with organizational needs. I understand that organizations do not really have payoffs; people do. However, individuals whose payoffs are not sufficiently aligned with the needs of the organization will be happier elsewhere.

I've organized my thoughts into a working model of RCL. Now, I want to test it out on someone. At this point, everyone has taken the SISP and Tracy has answered the SOS scale. Once I finish with Cluster and his capital items for the Hampton, I can get back to RCL.

I call Stan at the Hampton and ask him to send Cluster another copy of the room inventory that we send every quarter. I smile thinking about Cluster struggling with all of the abbreviations and codes, even though he has been shown numerous times.

Stan asks if I've heard the rumor that Cluster is going to drop Matrix, which I haven't. He says he doesn't want to work for Cluster and asks if I can find a place for him. He will even take a salary cut if need be—a great example of having payoffs other than money. I'll ask Ms. Long about other opportunities for him in Matrix: He has the potential to be a good General Manager. We agree to meet at the bar in the Diamond at around six o'clock to discuss what he wants to do next.

I call Dana Long and tell her about the Cluster rumor. She hasn't heard anything and will wait to hear from Cluster. She wants me to continue to do what is necessary for the Hampton.

I call Tracy and ask if she has about an hour to talk about some elements of RCL. She'll be tied up all day but can meet me around six or even for dinner if it's important. I tell her I'll check with her again some time this week.

It's time for me to work out. The uncertainty about the management contract for the Hampton is starting to get to me. An hour with my trainer will relieve the tension for a while; tension for me can be relieved by a hard workout. Stress, however, always seems to be lurking in the background, ready to show up the minute I let it. I understand that life is one problem or constraint after another and that the key to long-term sanity is recognizing the difference between problems and constraints.

My workout with Roger does the trick and I'm ready to talk to Stan when he walks into the bar around six o'clock. The Diamond lounge is a combination of old world elegance with high tech attributes. We find a quiet booth in the back, and a minute after we sit down, Sheila, one of our top-earning servers, walks up to take our orders.

Stan is almost speechless but orders a light beer. She turns to me, smiles knowingly, and says, "Your usual?" I say, "Please," and she glides off. Stan can't keep his eyes off her. I interrupt his gaze by asking, "How's business?" He is smiling until I ask him again, and then he frowns.

"Really good, but I got a disturbing call from Benny Hocking from the Green Tree," he finally replies.

"Yeah, I know him. What did he want?"

"He said he's going to be the new vice president of operations for Cluster and that I'll be reporting to him."

I can't help but laugh. "You're kidding?"

"No, I think he was serious, and I just cannot work for that low life."

"Stan, when I called Dana Long at Matrix today, she knew nothing about Cluster leaving Matrix. Benny has been known to lie almost without reason, remember; but I'll check again tomorrow with Long."

"Thanks. I need to know because I want out if he's going to be around all the time. His people hate him."

"Don't get too excited about this until we talk to Long. Why don't I set up a meeting with her for both of us tomorrow? We can check on what may be available for you in Matrix."

"I really appreciate your offer, but there's something else I want to talk to you about."

"Okay, go."

Just then Sheila returns to the table with our drinks. Stan smiles at her. When she leaves, he looks down, takes a sip of his beer, and finally says, "I don't know how to start. I guess two things got me thinking about the hotel business in general. One was the thought of working for people like Cluster, and now Benny. The second was taking the SISP."

"Go ahead," I say, wondering where this is going.

"Well, I really don't want to work for people like Cluster and Benny. In fact, I don't think I want to work in the industry any more. Seven-day weeks, every week, with no stopping except for interruptions from that jerk, are getting to me."

"Stan, is it just that you are stressed with the changes that might occur because of Cluster, or is it something else? When was the last time you got away from the hotel?" I ask.

"It's not that. It's the whole hassle with vendors, finding and keeping good people, the lack of caring on the part of employees, and the general atmosphere in the hotel business these days." Work environment can be a big payoff—positive or negative. "GMs are stealing each other's employees and cutting rates to take away business at every turn."

"Wow, you are burned out! But what about the SISP? You said that was the second reason you want to walk away from the industry."

Stan tells me about the initial shock he felt when he got the SISP results. At first he thought his answers had been scored incorrectly. But after looking at the details, he realized that not only did he have some areas of self-perceived low skill but, to his surprise, he had no interest in learning them. For example, he had no experience or training in food and beverage. Moreover, he had no interest in learning anything about it. And he realized that to make it to a place like the Diamond Creek Inn, he had to be very good in F & B. When he put his lack of skill and interest together, he realized he wanted to ignore F & B and some other functional areas, as well.

The more he thought about his current position and future positions, the more he realized that the hotel business was not for him. The constant pressure and never-ending activity of even a small hotel had burned him out. He couldn't imagine the pressures I must face every day.

At this point, I don't even bother to tell him that a big hotel also has a big staff and, in fact, my job is physically easier. I wonder how many GMs and department heads are burned out but can't afford to admit it to others or even to themselves. Think of the number of people just getting by every day, just waiting for retirement. What a sad way to live!

Stan is very upset so I tell him the story of a very pleasant man I met at a cocktail party about ten years ago. As we talked, the usual topic of work came up and, when I asked him what he did, he said that he was a senior loan officer for one of the big three banks in the country. To my utter surprise he added, "For another eight years, four months, and ten days." I laughed. He then proceeded to tell me how his retirement was going to go while saying nothing about what he actually did. He even mentioned that he would get 107% of his salary when he retired.

"Stan, you certainly don't want to spend the rest of your work life thinking about when you're going to retire. I'll do what I can to help you transition into whatever you want to do. Do you have any idea what that might be?"

"Well, according to the SISP results, I may want to learn about the mechanical and electrical aspects of maintenance."

"Really? Why's that?"

"I've always had an interest in hands-on work, but in my family, going to college and wearing a suit and tie were the overriding goals assigned to everyone—regardless of what any of us may have wanted. So, like a good son, I went to college and just sort of drifted into the hospitality business. But after taking the SISP, I started thinking about where this career path is taking me."

"Go on," I encourage.

"I always enjoyed working on cars until they became too complicated. So, I started thinking about what I really enjoy during my work day here and realized I really like helping the maintenance engineer solve problems. Sometimes, I spend two or even three hours actually doing the repairs. Until the SISP, I've always felt guilty about putting GM tasks on hold while I do fun stuff. Now, I understand what was not only drawing me to do repairs but what was keeping me from my GM role."

This is a great example of what happens when levels of interest in the tasks of a functional area influence performance. Good for Stan. I hope he finds what he's looking for.

Stan continues to talk and it's obvious that he's thrilled with his personal payoff discovery. He says that maintenance work for him can be challenging, stimulating, and thought-provoking and that the hand-eye coordination required of actually performing a repair is very satisfying. And every time he is confronted by a new repair problem he reviews the project in terms of all the trials, successes, and failures of past encounters with similar problems.

All in all, Stan says the maintenance work brings achievement, triumph, and satisfaction. As I listen to him, I realize, again, how wonderful it is to find something you really like to do and to go for it. He's willing to take a cut in position and salary to do what he really wants to do. No way to argue with that payoffs system!

Sheila comes back and asks if we want anything else. We decline and, as she walks away, Stan says, "However, I will miss some parts of the hotel business." We both laugh.

"Well, Stan, think about how you want to handle the transition. Let's talk tomorrow."

"I can't thank you enough, John, for making this so easy for me. I didn't know what to expect, but I figured that you would understand if anyone would."

I think that the three major elements have just been articulated by Stan:

1. I do have confidence in the organization's reward system.
2. I can do this job but I don't want to do it (skill and interest).
3. Moreover, what I get for doing this job isn't worth it to me (personal payoffs).

I walk Stan to the lobby doors and we stand there for a moment talking. From the number of people headed for the banquet rooms, it looks like the beginning of a busy night. "That excitement used to get me thinking I might like to do what you do, but no more," Stan says. "Now it just seems like more problems to face."

255

I smile. "It really is time for you to move on. And isn't it good that you found that out now rather than when you're forty-five and with too many obligations to be able to leave?"

"It sure is. Again, I can't thank you enough for all you've done for me." When he walks out, I go to see Ken about an overbooking problem.

Ken is all smiles. Two flight delays out of LaGuardia and Newark have saved the day. He took it upon himself to register every Blackwood/Diamond Creek VIP member that walked in, and with the transit walks, we'll come out looking very good for tonight. We'll find an answer to how the overbooking happened tomorrow.

It's close to seven thirty when I go back to the banquet halls to see what we have going tonight. It's been a long day with some strange turns of events and interesting outcomes—all part of my payoffs of being a GM, although now I know they are not the payoffs Stan was attracted to. A good lesson for me: *Do not assume that my payoffs will be universally the same for everyone.*

A brief discussion with the banquet manager gets me two bits of information. One is directly related to the hotel: We are feeding around 350 people sit-down tonight. The second is that Sam, as usual, is handling the commotion with great style. It seems he is always easy-going and relaxed. Calm or hectic, Sam is there and always in charge. I decide to ask him about his payoffs.

I ask if he has some time later, and he says that he can meet with me in about thirty minutes. In the meantime, I go to the restaurant for a soup and sandwich.

In those thirty minutes, I fight off the good-natured but serious hassling from the kitchen people about my eating too many sandwiches, read *USA Today,* and finish my meal. The soup is my compromise with the kitchen staff, who are concerned about my health.

I find Sam supervising the cleanup of the Blackwood Room. The group had an after-dinner speaker, and Sam asks me to follow him to the A/V storage room. He puts the equipment up and we go to the lounge to talk. As we walk in, Sheila sees me and says, "Back again?" I ask for a Diet Coke, and Sam orders coffee. I start the conversation by thanking him for all he does to make the hotel banquet area run so efficiently.

"Sam, why do you like your job so much?" I ask.

He looks at me with a smile. "What makes you think I like my job so much?"

A little stunned, I laugh. "Because you do it so well."

"Well, I like my job okay, but the truth is I picked it because I could get time off to go to PBA events."

"Really? You've been here for four years and I never knew that about you. Tell me more."

Sam proceeds to describe a world of work he has created at the Diamond that fits his personal payoffs almost perfectly. He's used our reward system and set up his department to achieve both the objectives of the hotel and his personal payoffs. Because I don't require specific punch-in times or days of work, he has trained his assistant to cover for him when he has to go to a tournament. He's been a pro bowler for ten years and this job provides him with the best opportunity to participate in events around the country. Because he's paid for hours worked, he feels comfortable.

He looks me straight in the eye and asks, "It's okay, isn't it?"

"Absolutely. In fact, how are you doing on the tour?"

Never ask people in love with their professions to tell you about them if you don't have two hours to listen. Sam goes on and on about what he loves about bowling. The joy in his voice makes his payoffs very clear.

"Well, I better get back to be sure we're ready for tomorrow morning," he says as he gets up to return to the banquet area. Sam has his priorities straight: When at work, be a star so you can continue to do what you really want to do. It's eight forty-five when I leave the hotel.

Wow! Big news tonight—two good people with two different perceptions about their worlds of work. Both have high skill levels in their current positions, but the interest level for one is marginal and for the other nonexistent. One sees the reward system as fitting perfectly with his personal payoffs; the other can no longer imagine a reward system that would attract him to hotel management. I'm tired as I pull into the garage.

The house seems big and silent and I think again about getting something smaller. I'm too tired to think about work anymore, so I get a glass of milk and a couple of cookies and go straight to bed. I channel surf for a while (as Seinfeld says, men don't care what's on television, they care about *what else* is on) and set the timer to turn off the set in thirty minutes.

CHAPTER EIGHTEEN

265 DAYS LATER

It is by teaching that we teach ourselves, by relating that we observe, by affirming that we examine, by showing that we look, by writing that we think.

Henri-Frédéric Amiel

    The last few months have brought the good, the bad, and the really ugly. As is my wont, I will start with the bad and the ugly. The ugly part occurred a few weeks after the rumor Benny started about Cluster taking over the Hampton. Turns out old Benny was right. Cluster, after getting the advice he needed from Matrix about franchise-required renovations, started arguing about everything.

One day I got a call from Dana Long. "Cluster called and said he could not understand the P & L we sent him," she said.

"He probably can't. He's never been able to read one before."

"He said you're not willing to help him, which is a lie, right?"

"Right. I've offered to help him, but he really is slow and is afraid to ask questions. He would rather be ignorant of the facts than ask a question. I'm not sure he can handle anything more complicated than fabricated numbers scribbled on the back of an envelope." (Everyone is in a race between retirement and obsolescence. How we handle that race is a good indicator of our character.)

"John, I hope you understand that we have all had enough of this guy. I am meeting with the president's people today to ask them to fire Cluster. I want you to know that if I get my way, I will have to reduce your second hotel incentive pay."

"I understand. Let me know what I should do."

Within ten days, Long called back and said she had met with the key people of Matrix. They had unanimously agreed to terminate Cluster for cause. They were going to meet with him at the end of the month and give him a ninety-day notice. I asked if she wanted me there, and she laughed and said that I would have to stand in line to tell him off. We laughed, and she said that actually they were going to try to do this in a civil and professional manner. Matrix did not need him bad-mouthing us in public.

However, Cluster did not wait for the end of the month. He hired a lawyer as soon as he thought he had the information he needed to fix the Hampton renovation crisis, the same crisis he created by not spending the necessary money. Without letting Matrix know, he called a meeting of the hotel staff and announced the change in management companies.

Stan told me the meeting was embarrassing to him and his staff. Cluster went on a swearing binge that lasted for three minutes. He promised great things from the new management company, and the staff thought things might actually be looking up, until he introduced Benny what's-his-name as the president of the new company, Cluster Management.

In the end, Matrix was out and Benny and Cluster were in. Wow, what a team—the shrimp and the blimp. The bad part was that I lost the extra money I was making for helping manage the Hampton. The good part was that I did not have to deal with Waldo Cluster any more.

Stan stayed on while he looked for other work. Since we had discussed how much he liked to work in the maintenance department, I set him up with someone that Vance had introduced me to, a guy whose company had provided us with HVAC/R service at the hotel. His name is Frank Linker, and he is the force behind TRIMCO. Frank is not only a superior engineer, but he is also a teacher at his local community college. The last time I talked to Stan he was in school learning from Frank, working part time for TRIMCO at what he loves, and a happy man. And life goes on.

Overall, life for me is better than it has been in a long time. There is a real sense of excitement and challenge for me. Not only is the Diamond Creek Inn doing well, but the staff and I seem to be more connected with each other. Reality Check for Leaders has done wonders for my hotel and is beginning to influence Matrix in a positive way.

I have presented two seminars with Dr. Spencer and five on my own. The response has been overwhelming. Every manager that I talk to wants to implement the program. The most difficult part is slowing down those not yet capable of utilizing RCL. As it turns out, not everyone is ready for RCL. There are a number of reasons, and we (Dr. Spencer and I) have worked on a method for letting those who need help understand the implementation challenges.

I like the idea that RCL is not for everyone. Moreover, I like the fact that people have to have enough interest in developing the skills necessary to implement the program—no free lunch.

After a number of seminars, I have come up with this sequence of activities:

1. Managers take the SISP to determine their interest and skill levels.
2. Next, the managers spend time with the SOS.
3. Finally, the manager must determine his or her personal payoffs.

First, managers take the SISP and use the results to establish individual plans of action for their own development. The SISP is not a plug-in program based on areas in need of improvement but, rather, is a tailored outline that reveals both the perceived skill areas and the specific interests of the individual respondents. In my view, it's a waste of time to force people to learn skills that have no personal payoffs relative to their real interests.

And I agree with Buckingham and Clifton in their book, *Now, Discover Your Strengths*:

> Unfortunately, most of us have little sense of our talents and strengths. Instead guided by our parents, by our teachers, by our managers, and by psychology's fascination with pathology, we become experts in our weaknesses and spend our lives trying to repair these flaws, while our strengths lie dormant and neglected.

Second, managers spend time with the SOS, responding to statements about their perceptions of the organization's reward system. An important factor in this part of RCL is the individual's perception of what constitutes the organization's reward system for behavior/performance.

If managers do not believe that the company rewards performance of specific behaviors, then all progress is put on hold until that perception is corrected. The SOS is a useful tool for any company interested in knowing more about how their people perceive the organization's reward system.

However, the most important aspect of this element of RCL is the managers' understanding of how much they influence the employees' perceptions of the organization's reward system. Additionally, managers are responsible for how department heads convey to their employees the company's reward system for performance. Employees' perceptions are the only reality.

Without the understanding that perception is the only reality, any leadership method will fade quickly into just another "flavor-of-the-month," fix-it-all management tool. Any leadership approach that does not separate the organizational reward system from the leader reward system will become an exercise in "playing at motivating people" instead of a real method of understanding why people behave the way they do.

Organizations can put up posters, send employees to hear motivational speakers, and talk a good game of rewards for performance. The reality is that employees can learn new and useful methods of working with people, but if they return to an organization that rewards the status quo, then in a short period of time they will revert to their former behaviors. Moreover, a company can preach quality as the first priority, but if it responds only to the P & L, employees will respond in kind. I know owners who talk of quality but, when the money is spent, buy bedding and drapes rather than mattresses. That indicates they are more interested in outward appearances than the stability of sound guest satisfaction, regardless of what they say.

Third, the manager must determine his or her payoffs. This process is both simple and complicated. It should be noted that what individuals really believe to be important in life seems to be the driving force in all their behavior. While that is true, a problem in detailing those specific payoffs arises because of the nature of people. We don't often take the time to understand our payoffs.

The expression that people throw away their lives day by day waiting for the train to come in has always impressed me as a good way to describe one of the payoff dilemmas. I know people who promise themselves that as soon as (fill in the change) occurs, they will start doing (fill in the payoff). As soon as (fill in the name) starts behaving in a certain way, then their personal lives will be perfect (payoff). Similarly, as soon as the supervisor stops (fill in the behavior), then their jobs will be great (payoff). Once the train comes in, I will be happy, never really understanding that it is not only what I think, feel, or want that matters, but also what I actually *do*.

Managers who know what payoffs are important to themselves can then begin to understand what payoffs are important to their people. Without one, there cannot be the other.

Once managers or leaders understand their own payoffs, they also understand that the things, feelings, or behaviors that influence them may not necessarily influence others. Knowing that people have their own personal payoffs and that these payoffs can change depending on the situation is an important element of understanding the behavior of others.

And so we have three key steps to understanding why people behave the way they do. The idea has come full circle. I had originally thought RCL was just another management theory that would disappear into the wilderness of other motivational theories. What I've discovered over the last ten months is that RCL provides a real understanding of human behavior.

It is a few minutes before nine as I walk toward the meeting room set up for me to teach RCL. The participants for today's seminar are a group of managers in various hotel departments. Matrix has permitted me to branch out with my teaching (the company's reward system being manifested in the form of Dana Long allowing me to do this.) I hold most of the seminars at the Diamond and do about one per month.

The group of about twenty-five participants is having coffee and talking. I go over the roster in my mind as I walk in and start saying hello. I like to say hello to people before starting a session to avoid that uncomfortable "Good morning class" start-up where people are obligated to act like eight-year-olds and answer in unison.

This group is made up of general managers, directors of sales, and front and back office managers. They are key people in important positions in various hotels throughout the Southeast. They represent franchise brands with 400-plus rooms and suites, like The Diamond Creek Inn, as well as 100-room independent operations. The overriding, single common element is quality. No matter the size, each represents a management company's or owner's commitment to quality management.

After a few programs that started with Matrix, I've discovered that organizations interested enough in their people to expose them to RCL also have a high regard for their properties and the people working there. Almost without exception, their properties' physical appearance and guest satisfaction scores match the satisfaction of the personnel. It seems to me that RCL equals quality, which equals potential profits.

After checking my appearance in the restroom and getting a cup of coffee, I am ready to go. The most dynamic professor I ever met once told me, when we were talking about effective teachers, that if you do not check your appearance before you walk into a classroom, you should get out of teaching because you don't care anymore.

As I walk to the front of the room, people start looking for their names printed on cards. I notice the age range is from mid-twenties to mid-fifties. I start by asking them to spend a few minutes telling us how they got to where they are today.

After everyone has completed the introductions, I pass out their individual results from the SISP. Their results are compared to the responses of the thousands of working managers that have taken the profile. I explain that the various interests and skills have been cross-referenced by years of service, functional areas, position, and age. I spend about an hour and a half discussing what the results may mean to the people in the room. Each has more questions than I can answer in the time I have allowed for this segment.

We discuss the results in terms of four categories of interest and skill. Thus, if an individual scores *High Interest and High Skill* in any functional area, that person will benefit from capitalizing on those talents and skills further. It seems obvious, but often people neglect something they really enjoy and excel at doing because they have been conditioned to look for more. If they devote time and effort to strengthening their skills, they will be rewarded and happy about the payoff.

If a person scores *High Skill and Low Interest* in an area, the first question to ask is, "Why aren't they interested in pursuing something that they're very good at doing?"

I tell the group about Bill, who is considered eccentric by most. He marches to the beat of a different drummer and always acts to pursue personal payoffs rather than goals dictated by society. His view of his world can be explained by his story.

266

Bill was told on a Friday afternoon that, starting Monday, he would become an assistant senior vice president of computing at a large financial institution. His office would be moved to just one away from the corner office; the corner office signified to everyone who the boss was. This company had a reward system that involved, among other things, a complicated series of desktop finishes and offices that carried a position status ending at the corner office.

Bill spent the weekend thinking about his promotion and his future with the company. He walked into the senior vice president's office on Monday and resigned. His reason: He found his current job to be very unchallenging and believed that the next one would be even less challenging. Therefore, he had decided to go to graduate school and find something else to do. He walked away from a position for which he was highly skilled and highly paid but had no interest in doing. Thus, the High Skill-Low Interest question was answered for him.

We then talk about the individual with a *High Interest and Low Skill* level. Often the low skill level combined with high interest reflects a lack of exposure to the area rather than an inability to perform the tasks. When people discover this result in the hotel business, they are fortunate in that all competent management companies encourage people to cross-train in as many areas of the hotel as possible.

I have heard employees say, for example, "I really like to cook and plan menus for parties at home, so I bet I would be good as an F & B director." When they're given the opportunity to work in a commercial kitchen serving hundreds of people day and night, the fascination with F & B sometimes fades. On the other hand, sometimes the interest intensifies and a real F & B star is created. In any event, it's important for the person scoring *High Interest* in any functional area to strengthen the skills necessary for the details of the required tasks. If perceived skill level is low, education and experience will raise the level higher. I recommend some on-the-job training before spending time and resources on educational programs.

Finally, when an individual scores *Low Skill and Low Interest* in a functional area or areas, the person needs to face reality and circumvent the situation. While it may seem obvious, many people are caught in positions they are ill suited to perform. And more important, they are not interested in those positions.

The extremely high turnover rate in the hotel business creates openings for people who are not prepared. Some hotels experience more than a fifty percent turnover rate in management positions in a year. That can create unfortunate opportunities for some individuals—unfortunate in the sense that they are not prepared at the appropriate skill level and often have not experienced the particular job. They are thrown into positions without proper training and soon find that the tasks are not what they expected.

How often has an exceptional rooms inspector been placed in a position as Executive Housekeeper (Ex.Hsk.), simply because the person is next in line for promotion or is good at inspection? The inspector accepts the promotion because our culture encourages that type of thinking and feeling. The GM believes that moving someone up in the organization is a faster and easier answer than hiring externally and that it is easier to find a new room inspector than a new Ex.Hsk. Sometimes within two months, both parties know that the promotion was a mistake.

Then the problem for both is getting out of the dilemma. Each side struggles with the situation in which, for example, the employee may not be interested in all the paperwork involved in being Ex.Hsk., and the GM hesitates to admit having made a mistake in promoting the rooms inspector. The GM believes that with a little help the Ex.Hsk. will improve their administrative skills.

The new Ex.Hsk. does not want to step down and feels the frustration of not knowing what to do.

And it is not as if the new Ex.Hsk. can simply close the hotel in order to learn the administrative side of the business. The hotel business never stops to take a break. While I dislike the expression "24/7" because it is overused, the expression "24/7/365" does describe a permanent characteristic of the hotel business. As a result, business goes on and mistakes are made. Other department heads begin to complain about the lack of information coming out of the housekeeping department. The front desk needs room availability. Guests are made to wait unnecessarily. The problems mount and the effective rooms inspector becomes the ineffectual Ex.Hsk. Tensions mount at staff meetings and everyone begins to feel the stress. What seemed an easy and fast fix to the GM at the time has turned into a complicated series of miscommunications, embarrassments, and inter-departmental conflicts. If the GM had thought about the rooms inspector's promotion in terms of RCL, a different decision would have been made.

People in seminars can only sit and absorb information for so long, and we are well past most participants' thresholds for maintaining full concentration. I never delude myself into believing that everyone who attends a seminar is interested and/or skilled enough to understand the concepts of RCL.

Some people are here because it's their turn to have a day off. Others are here because they are being groomed for a higher position. Some companies use a seminar as a way of notifying other people in the organization of the transition that is about to occur. I believe that most people are here because they want a better way to lead their people. I always enjoy trying to guess who wants what payoff—a new way to lead, a status symbol, or a day off.

During the break, people talk to each other about their SISP results. I smile because I know that Directions

Inc., the company that developed the profile, has devoted a considerable amount of time and effort to keeping the responses of individuals confidential. Yet, here I have people openly sharing with one another. Ah, the magic of eventual anonymity—although I must admit that when the Matrix people participated, they too were open with each other. The willingness to talk about results of this nature is directly related to the trust people have in their working environment—which is another way of saying that individuals' attitudes toward openness are determined by the reward system they recognize.

I watch as five or six people walk outside to smoke. Others check voicemails and make calls—what a shame that most people can't free up just a few hours to clear their minds and absorb new information. I wonder if that behavior is of their own making or is a product of their company's reward system.

YOU SHOULD KNOW

Some stress junkies take on all burdens. Is it to lessen the stress of others or to increase their own?

Just then my cell phone rings, and I laugh as I shut it off. I have to practice what I preach. The hotel business brings new surprises and challenges almost every hour of almost every day. I'm tempted to find out who called, but I pass on the idea and go back inside the meeting room. I want to get started on the SOS results.

Tracy walks into the meeting room and asks if I have time tomorrow morning to discuss some room displacement issues. We agree to meet at nine o'clock, and she leaves.

The next segment I cover is the perceived reward system. We talk about the various reward systems and how they influence individual behavior.

I start the discussion by asking if anyone can help me define an organization's reward system. The general manager of a hundred-room Days Inn says that the reward system is what you get for doing your work. A director of sales from a Hilton Garden Inn says a reward system is a number of different items that make up the total compensation package an individual receives when working for a specific company. A district manager for a medium-sized management company suggests his organization's reward system is the sum total of the benefits described in the company policies and procedures manual. I ask him if he thinks about negative rewards. He smiles. "Sure, it's what happens when you don't follow the rules."

I wonder out loud about how many good ideas are killed on the spot when a manager hearing a new idea from an employee decides, "I can't get into trouble with my boss if I say no to trying this new idea." Alternatively, how many creative ideas for change from line people are quashed by the phrase, "We won't change because I am the boss and I know best."?

I ask the group to vote on the three responses to my question about defining a reward system, but before I can count hands, a woman who is about to become an assistant food and beverage director for a full service Holiday Inn speaks up. "I want to add another answer before we vote."

Her name is Kelly. She thinks that a company's reward system is made up of everything that influences the way people feel about their jobs. I ask her to go on. The company she works for provides her with the opportunity to develop her leadership skills by paying for this seminar.

She first developed an interest in food and beverage when she was helping in the kitchen one night when they were slammed with a convention and bus tour arrival all at once. Kelly had been a reservations manager and after doing some company-encouraged cross training by working with the kitchen manager, she asked to be transferred to F & B. After an additional four months of working in all areas of F & B, she and the director decided her first position would be assistant F & B director. The encouragement she received from her company to develop new skills based on her interests is an important part of what she believes is the company's reward system. I think the SISP may have identified her potential sooner.

Other people start suggesting additional elements of their companies' reward systems. After about thirty minutes, the original statements seem less than inclusive. I suggest that a review of their individual SOS scores may prove interesting and helpful in our discussion. As I distribute the results, the attention level of the group increases even more.

Given that the majority of the participants represent different organizations, a lively exchange of ideas and results starts. I let them talk to each other for about ten minutes and then ask for their attention. For the next hour, we discuss individual and group results, and they compare their results to the norms that have been established. The group concludes the following:

1. An organization's reward system can be determined by a combination of the following elements:
   a. The written and formal policy and procedures of an organization.
   b. The informal organizational behavior established over time and by leaders.
2. An organization's reward system is only as good as the immediate supervisor.
3. An individual's perception of the reward system is the only reality.

4. To be effective, the organization's reward system must match a significant number of the individual's important personal payoffs.

I conclude the discussion of organizational reward systems by explaining that effective leaders always understand that their behavior is a major determinant in how employees view the entire organization. People are often heard to say, "This company is great," when what they mean is, "My boss understands what I need and helps me get it" (payoffs). Conversely, when top level managers say, "Working for XYZ Management is horrible," they really mean that the president or someone else in a leadership position is a jerk.

YOU SHOULD KNOW

Leadership means both getting the best possible performance from people and giving them what they want.

An argument can be made that, with enough information presented to employees, an organization's reward system can be clearly defined. The reality is that the perception of rewards and punishments changes as the leadership of the system changes. It is understandable that leaders are frustrated by the seeming lack of response to certain offers of rewards to their employees. The problem may not be the written explanation of the reward but rather an individual manager's approach to explaining the payoff.

A number of motivation professionals have suggested the need for an employee to have confidence in a hotel's or management company's formal reward system. The contention is that unless the employee can be assured of rewards for specific behavior, performance will suffer.

"I believe, however," I explain to the group, "that any employee in a hotel is aware of how the stated reward system is really implemented. The problem with confidence in a management company's reward system is just that some employees know exactly what to expcct from their leaders, and they don't like it."

It's time to take a break. Some of the smokers are getting twitchy, and the group deserves a chance to absorb what we've talked about before we start on personal payoffs.

I'm almost done and so far it's been great fun for me. I hope it has been for them, too.

CHAPTER NINETEEN

THE HOME STRETCH

A great book should leave you with many experiences, and slightly exhausted at the end.

William Styron

      I start the next session by suggesting that everyone pursues personal payoffs, a statement which draws varied and strong reactions. Some think the statement is too harsh, while others agree that it makes sense to look at people in terms of pursuing personal payoffs. I ask the group to take fifteen minutes and make a list (not to be shared) of what their payoffs are.

      The question of personal rewards, or payoffs, has been around in one form or another for centuries. Adam Smith described the benefits of an invisible hand guiding capitalist society. He believed that if individuals pursued their self-interests (payoffs), society as a whole would benefit. Maslow described the pyramid of payoffs people pursued, ranging from food, water, and sex to self-actualization. Countless others have described payoffs as ranging from the warm feeling someone gets when helping others to good old-fashioned revenge.

Both positive and negative payoffs influence behavior; avoiding negative payoffs is as rational as seeking positive ones. Leaders create work environments that encourage pursuit of some payoffs and avoidance of others. When people are pursuing personal payoffs, the organization has a chance to operate in an open and productive manner. However, when leadership style promotes the avoidance of negative payoffs, then a great deal of valuable time will be spent in self-protection activities. Remember, if a leader says, "No, we can't do it another way," then that leader can't get into trouble.

In all work environments, individuals come to the organization with personal payoffs established. Determining those payoffs will be key to the manager's understanding of why his or her people behave the way they do. Thus, the question becomes: How do leaders determine the payoffs of their people?

Generally, the extent to which individuals are willing to discuss their personal payoffs will fall into one of four categories:

1. Payoffs that people are willing to tell most people (common knowledge).
2. Payoffs that people are willing to tell some people (insightful knowledge).
3. Payoffs that people are willing to share with a very few people (intimate details).
4. Payoffs that people are not willing to share with anyone, often including themselves (best left to those in the social sciences).

People are initially willing to share with a leader all of the general aspects of their personal payoffs. In the proper environment, they will discuss their common knowledge payoffs in more detail. We may conclude from the last two statements that the task of ascertaining the necessary information about an individual's payoffs is relatively easy. However, there are a few roadblocks to what seems to be a straightforward task.

Roadblock One: We hear what we want to hear. As managers and leaders, we have our own personal payoffs and have a vested interest in believing those payoffs are the best. Often when we listen to others talk about their payoffs, we hear their words filtered through our perceptions of our rational worlds. If they do not fit our worlds, we tend not to hear them.

Roadblock Two: Understanding why people behave the way they do requires time and effort. As managers, we become so busy fixing the people problems we have that we cut short the time for opportunities to focus on what motivates a specific person. The individuals we ignore now will take more time later.

Roadblock Three: We don't recognize the true payoff. Sometimes people are so candid that their responses are discounted. My banquet manager, who works not to advance in the hotel industry but in the Professional Bowling Association Tour, is a great example. Conversely, some people don't know how to express their personal payoffs in logical, or even understandable, forms. For example, making the statement, "I would rather work with numbers than with people," may seem like a negative approach to applying for a job, unless it is for the night auditor position.

The problems encountered in recognizing an individual's true payoffs can be overcome with ... Hello! Pay attention.

I often wonder how long I can really listen with a focused mind to anyone. The truth is that after about ten minutes I start to add other bits of information to what I'm hearing: interesting shirt, not too smart, what was the

ADR today? We all let our minds wander after a relatively short time.

If a night auditor job seems boring, it is because most people cannot see the payoff auditors get by solving the accounting problems and puzzles created by others. Similarly, if the payoffs of the person you are talking to don't match yours, the question you should ask yourself is, "What is special about their payoffs to them?" The question should *not* be, "Why are their payoffs wrong?" Finally, when you take the time to understand the individual's payoffs today, you will save considerable time and frustration in the future. The key is being willing to allocate enough time to make payoff recognition successful.

As I continue to discuss with the group this last part of RCL, I realize that I haven't specified the payoffs people aspire to in their worlds. I tell them that I have thought for a long time about creating a personal payoff list for people to use; but I've concluded that it makes more sense to ask people what they want out of life instead of boxing them into personal payoff categories. I believe it's enough to distinguish the category of payoffs in terms of accessibility. The reality is that the payoffs people only share with a very few people, or none at all, are best left to intimate relationships and professionals. For me, getting to the major common knowledge payoffs and working toward the share-with-some payoffs is more than enough to make RCL work.

The group agrees and, after a summary of all three elements of RCL, they break into pairs to practice with each other. As they are talking, I walk around the room and listen to the various conversations. I have selected pairs at random and am happy to see that, regardless of the comparative job position, the matches are interesting and lively. In addition, because they are "permanent" strangers—people who will more than likely not be co-workers—the atmosphere is open and inviting. (I have no illusions that people who work together have the same degree of openness.) The group has a free-flowing discussion about personal payoffs, rewards, and interest and skill levels. Within an hour, the pairs have each developed RCL characterizations of each other. They are able to describe their team partners in terms of

1. Skills and interests relative to the hotel business
2. Their partner's perceptions of the organization's reward system
3. Individual personal payoffs

I'm always pleased when I realize how much people enjoy learning about human behavior in general and themselves specifically. They seem to marvel at the clarity of the understanding associated with RCL. We also discuss the feelings of achievement associated with comprehending the elements of the approach.

It's clear to most that RCL is not for everyone. One of the best lines Ron White delivers is, "We got aspirins for headaches, diets for weight problems, doctors for our health, and beauty shops for looks but—you can't fix stupid."

By the end of the day, we are all tired. From what I am hearing, the day has been productive and worthwhile to most. As usual, two or three people just wanted a day away from the office. The RCL program is way too much work for someone accustomed to minimally acceptable behavior. For the marginal people, RCL doesn't provide sufficient payoffs for the behavior required. And life goes on.

It is close to five o'clock when we finish, and I get a round of applause. I have found applause and the occasional wave of laughter to be unexpected payoffs of public speaking. People should get a round of applause for

279

doing a good job and not just for performing on a stage, court, or field. Applaud more, fight less! (Or maybe not.)

A few people in the group invite me to have a drink in the bar. Although I really want to be alone after all this togetherness today, I agree.

As I walk into the bar, I'm reminded of a quote by Andrew Wyeth. When he was asked to describe people's reactions to the drawing of Helga sitting by a tree, he answered with a question, "I think anything like that—which is contemplative, silent, shows a person alone—people always feel is sad. Is it because we've lost the art of being alone?" I think most people do not appreciate the payoffs associated with solitude. We seem, as a society, to desire less and less time alone. Televisions at home, radios in the car, iPods when we walk, and, of course, the ever ubiquitous cell phones—all designed to keep us from being alone. I know people who fill their own and their families' days and nights with activities that guarantee they will not be alone. I have often thought about trying to understand the fear of being alone that some people have, but not now.

We sit in the bar and talk about the seminar and the expectations they will bring back to their organizations. Once again, the reward systems of their various organizations become the focal point of discussion. From what I've gathered from similar discussions with group participants, most companies make some effort to develop their people. The activities designed to improve leadership skills range from teaching new leadership theories to on-the-job training in which people are paired with managers who are viewed as strong leaders.

Individuals participating in leadership seminars are continually told that the latest management theory is the answer to all their problems, while those in on-the-job training situations are given only one approach to understanding behavior. People have told me of leadership styles that range from "my way or the highway" to seminars that preach consensus management, which is psychobabble for no leadership at all.

Regardless of an organization's approach to leadership training for its managers, if any one of the three RCL elements is missing, the results will be short-term at best, or more than likely, nonexistent. The combination of elements in RCL provides any competent formal or informal leader with a systematic, precise view of what makes people behave the way they do. With the knowledge collected using RCL, expectations about behavior in the work place can be realistic, and any differences between expected and real behavior can be understood.

I always try to make it clear to students of RCL that understanding behavior and tolerating it are two separate and distinct outcomes. The entire issue of cutting losses is not given enough attention. With a clear picture of what a manager can expect from an individual, there is no reason to prolong a lost cause. Remember, the activity with the lowest percentage of success is attempting to alter a person's behavior against that individual's will.

Our group breaks up around six thirty, and I feel as if I have done a full day's work and then some. I decide to pass on going to my office and leave for home. Too tired to work out and too keyed up to really rest, I drive home in that haze of satisfaction that comes to me when I teach well. The better I understand my personal skill and interest levels, my view of the organization's reward system, and my personal payoffs, the more I realize how good my situation is. I have the opportunity to run a first class hotel, while also having an additional creative outlet with my public speaking.

Teaching provides me with a number of payoffs: I love the challenge of speaking before a group; I enjoy the recognition and appreciation of the individuals who attend the seminars; and I relish the simple joy of learning more about human behavior.

The most exciting part of the process is that Matrix, represented by Dana Long, has whole-heartedly adopted the RCL approach for all of its managers. Long, in fact, conveys the company's image; her behavior defines my perception of Matrix. Organization leaders should heed the truth embodied by this example. Her support and encouragement pushed the president to allocate the funds and time necessary for all managers at all levels to participate in RCL. I volunteer to teach the RCL seminars to Matrix people, and Long allows me time off to teach RCL to hospitality managers working outside of Matrix.

The feedback from people who have participated in the seminars is overwhelmingly positive. While a few people think it's too much to learn, the majority appreciate the payoffs they get from employing RCL. I have a collection of thank you letters from people who describe the positive changes that have occurred because of their implementing RCL. Other letters describe how RCL has helped them identify potential behavior problems before they happen.

The Diamond Creek Inn continues to recover along with the Charlotte economy. Business is good and the atmosphere in the hotel matches the positive outlook. The relatively newly reorganized CVB is doing an outstanding job. Employees feel secure about their jobs, and one result is that they treat guests with more enthusiasm. The hotel's general atmosphere is characterized by a sense of moving forward and doing well.

I, for one, have become a true believer in RCL as a better way to get things done. We all have made the Performance Elements our own: the examination of individual interest and skill levels, a real understanding of the reward system, and identification of the personal payoffs that influence work behavior. We also cut our losses with people who cannot produce when given the

282

opportunity. All in all, RCL has made the Diamond Creek Inn an effective, productive, money-making business.

Dr. Spencer and I continue to stay in touch, although his schedule is so full that he's been unable to participate in many of the seminars. With his help and my interest in learning more, I've broadened my thinking concerning the uses of RCL.

For example, I've begun to appreciate that the SISP, with some word changes, may be useful to high school students in determining what future career directions they may consider. Our country continues to move toward centralized testing, and the dropout rate in some high schools approaches fifty percent, as young people perceive the reasons for staying in school to be of diminishing importance. I have contacted Directions, Inc., about using the SISP in colleges and high schools. The president seems interested and plans to visit Charlotte in the near future to talk about potential uses for the profile.

I also realize that the SOS can be a significant management tool for hotels, management companies, and franchisers. Often leaders assume that their own beliefs about the relationship between work behavior and rewards are also held by everyone else in the organization. The truth is that people's individual perceptions of the reward system of an organization represent the only reality. It does not matter what leaders say about what level of performance will equal what level of reward; all that matters is what people *believe* to be true about the rewards/payoffs.

Finally, the more I deal with personal payoffs, the more I realize that people do not spend enough time thinking about their own personal payoffs. I wonder if the pace of life as accepted by the vast majority of people precludes enough alone time to ponder this vital question. Do people fill their lives with gadgets, activities, and lots of friends to avoid thinking about themselves? People spend so much time protecting, maintaining, and enhancing their self-images that they don't have time to think about what really makes them happy.

I have decided that I get a great deal of satisfaction out of helping people understand their behavior. Put differently, providing people with insight into the way they think, feel and behave can be a challenging and rewarding experience for them and me. The fact of the matter is that understanding how organizations function is also a great payoff. Moreover, the combination of understanding individual and organizational behavior is a powerful force in maximizing leadership behavior. Now, there is a way to spend productive and rewarding work time.

Epilogue

It's around four o'clock when we get home from work. My new job at Matrix combines the rewards of teaching with the administration/leadership of all the education programs and training required of hotel employees. I am even co-authoring a book. I try to write at least thirty minutes each day and, if I have more things to say, I write more. If not, I stop and go on to something else. I think this book will convey some understanding about why people behave the way they do, but it will not be stuffy. (In my research, I have actually come across a book that discusses human conflict with organizational objectives described as the bifurcation of sub-unit goals.) I want my book to be readable and enjoyable. While learning is always work, it does not have to be pretentious.

I continue to go into work early. However, unlike a hotel, the corporate offices close at five unless there is a problem. The time flexibility offered by Matrix gives me a tremendous payoff.

On days like today when the forecast calls for snow, I can come home early. I start a fire to take the chill out of the air while she goes in the kitchen. We have been living together for a few months but it seems like years. As it turns out, she is not only beautiful but very bright. What I like is that I can be alone with her for hours without the need to say anything. We both like cars, although she prefers BMWs to Porsches. And spending nights in front of a fire has turned out to be our favorite thing to do together. As I think about the house and yard, my desire to move diminishes after every walk we take. It seems we go every place together, including work. And I don't feel as alone anymore. I guess we were meant to be together.

I sit back, look out to see if the snow has started, and begin to work on the book Mark Spencer and I are writing about leading volunteers. I am up to chapter five, and so far, the book seems to be flowing in the right direction. With my years of community volunteer work and his knowledge of behavior, we should be able to provide insight to all those people who work with and lead volunteer groups, committees, and non-profit organizations.

I recall an incident that I will use to illustrate the concept that the individual's perception of a situation is the only reality. As a backdrop for observing volunteer behavior, I am using a major celebrity golf tournament that I created. Being the first General Chairman of the tournament held at a prestigious private country club in North Carolina, I had the opportunity to experience significant differences in the personal payoffs, rewarded behaviors, and interest and skill levels of the wonderful people who actually made the tournament happen.

I think about how the principles of RCL will work for any endeavor, regardless of the mission. With some introspection, I am also working on concepts to improve the leadership of volunteers in charity drives, homeowners associations, country club boards, educational institution boards of trustees, and the various community volunteer groups that I have worked with over the years. This book will provide leaders of volunteers with insight into the way well-intentioned helpers can be directed to maximize performance and accomplish stated objectives.

It's close to six when she comes into the study and sits down across from me. I ask her if she has found anything interesting in the house, and she responds by wagging her tail and putting her head on my lap. Diamond, the beautiful Bernese Mountain dog that I got for my birthday, settles down in front of the fire and quickly goes to sleep.

For now, I'm going to sit back and enjoy the payoffs I get by understanding and applying Reality Check Leadership. I hope you soon begin to enjoy the same advantage. And life goes on.

Take care of yourself,

John

To my Mother,
Angeline Mary Scoppechio Schilagi

CHAPTER	ATTRIBUTION
1	Ellen Glasgow, American novelist (1873–1945); from *The Woman Within,* 1954.
2	Thomas Szasz, U.S. psychiatrist (b.1920); from *The Second Sin,* 1973.
3	George Gordon Byron, English poet (1788–1824); from *Byron's Letters and Journals.*
4	Titus Livius (Livy), Roman Historian (59 B.C.–A.D. 17); from *Histories, IV.*
5	George Crabbe, British clergyman and poet (1754–1832); from *The Borough,* 1810.
6	Kahlil Gibran, U.S. actor (1873–1934); from *My Own Story,* 1934.
7	Alice Foote MacDougall, U.S. businesswoman (1867–1945); from *The Autobiography of a Business Woman,* 1928.
8	Fran Lebowitz, U.S. humorist (b. 1950); from *Social Studies,* 1981.
9	W.C. Fields, U.S. screen actor (1879–1946); from *Halliwell's Filmgoer's Companion,* 1995.
10	James P. Comer, U.S. psychiatrist (b. 1934); from *School Power,* 1980.

11   Stanley I. Greenspan, U.S. clinical professor of psychiatry and behavioral sciences, author (b. 1941); from *Playground Politics*, 1993.

12   Mason Cooley, U.S. aphorist (b. 1927); from *City Aphorisms*, 1990.

13   Alice S. Rossi, U.S. sociologist (b. 1922); from *Dissent*, 1970.

14   Ralph Waldo Emerson, U.S. essayist, poet, and philosopher (1803–1882); from *Journals*, entry for Nov. 8, 1838.

15   Václav Havel, Czechoslovakian playwright and president (b. 1936); from *Disturbing the Peace*, 1986.

16   Albert Einstein, German-born U.S. theoretical physicist (1879–1955); from *Out of My Later Years*, 1950.

17   Erich Fromm, U.S. psychologist (1900–1980); from *Escape from Freedom*, 1941.

18   Henri-Frédéric Amiel, Swiss philosopher and poet (1821–1881); from *Journal Intime*, entry for Oct. 27, 1853.

19   William Styron, U.S. novelist (1925–2006); from interview in *Writers at Work*, 1958.

REFERENCES AND ACKNOWLEDGEMENTS

BATES, FREDRICK L. Bates developed the original concept of the potential variables that influence the difference between real and expected behavior. His text, *Sociopolitical Ecology: Human Systems and Ecological Fields* (Chapel Hill, NC: Plenum Publishing Corporation, 2006) is the essence of his work on human interaction, situation, and personality.

BONDANELLA, PETER, and MARK MUSA. *Machiavelli, Translated and Edited* (New York, NY: Penguin Books). An exploration into the meaning his important works brought to political and individual thought. In the 450 years since his death, his writings continue to contribute to the understanding of human behavior.

BUCKINGHAM, MARCUS, and DONALD O. CLIFTON, Ph.D. *Now, Discover Your Strengths.* (New York, NY: Free Press, 2001). An interesting approach to improving performance by identifying individual talents and building on personal strengths.

CAMPBELL, DAVID, Ph.D. The idea of dividing areas of Interest and Skill into a Matrix of suggested actions was originally developed by David P. Campbell, Ph.D., in the *Campbell Interest and Skill Survey (CISS)* (Allen, TX: NCS Pearson, Inc., 1988). Also read, *If I'm in Charge Here, Why Is Everybody Laughing?* (Argus Communications, 1980).

CARTER, STEVEN, and JULIA SOKOL. *Lives Without Balance: When You're Giving Everything You've Got and Still Not Getting What You Hoped For* (New York, NY: Villard Books, 1992). Approaches the dysfunction aspects of the personal payoff vs. the organization reward system. Explores the view that declining rewards for our efforts are dramatically disproportionate to the time and energy we invest.

CHAMPION, JOHN M., and JOHN H. JAMES. *Critical Incidents in Management: Decision and Policy Issues* (Tallassee, FL: Irwin Professional Publishing, 1988). A series of relevant management incidents that provide the reader with incident analysis centered on developing a philosophy of thought and a personal value system. Particular attention is given to the Production Slowdown incident analyzed by Frank J. Schilagi, Ph.D.

CIALDINI, ROBERT B. *Influence: How and Why People Agree to Things* (New York, NY: William Morrow and Company, 1993). A fascinating look into the fundamental patterns that individuals use to persuade others, as well as the motivations of the persuaders and the persuaded.

CLARK, KENNETH E., MIRIAM B. CLARK, ROBERT R. ALBRIGHT, CENTER FOR CREATIVE LEADERSHIP, and PSYCHOLOGICAL CORPORATION, eds. *Measures of Leadership* (West Orange, NJ: Leadership Library of America, 1990). A useful resource for reviewing the thinking of experts in the field of leadership. The editors aim to dispel myths and the then common misconceptions. Although the attempt is made to challenge conventional views of leadership and management, the succeeding years proved that experts were not ready to move in a more realistic direction.

CRICHTON, MICHAEL. *Next* (New York, NY: HarperCollins, 2006). Offers an insightful view of the age-old discussion of genes vs. the environment. Consider that humans and chimpanzees differ in only 400 genes. The idea that behavior can be influenced by personality, situations, and human interaction becomes a key to understanding expectations about the way we think, feel, and behave.

The important conclusion is that it has never been proven that a single gene causes behavior.

FUKUYAMA, FRANCIS. *The Great Disruption: Human Nature and the Reconstitution of Social Order* (New York, NY: Free Press, 2000). A brilliant work of analysis for anyone interested in understanding the destructive changes associated with our culture's transformation from industrial to informational and service-based. The insights generated provide the reader with a thorough knowledge of the world created by social change.

GOLEMAN, DANIEL. *Vital Lies, Simple Truths: The Psychology of Self-deception* (New York, NY: Simon & Schuster, 1985). A useful background for understanding the concept of RCL. The author provides insight into how individuals create their own world and then behave rationally in that world. For example: "Everything we perceive is sorted, filtered and censored by our unconscious mind—before it reaches awareness. As a result as much as 99 percent is never even registered."

HAYES, MERWYN A., Ph.D. Dr.Hayes is a talented teacher of communication skills and the CEO and President of the Hayes Group International, Inc. His insights into effective communications have benefited scores of corporations and individuals.

KAGAN, JEROME. *An Argument for Mind* (Harrisonburg, VA: Yale University Press, 2006). Easily the most intellectually beneficial work devoted to understanding why the reductionistic aspirations of modern psychologists are not likely to be fulfilled. Kagan provides the reader with a clear understanding of why behaviorism and Freudianism, the two most dominant psychological paradigms, have failed. Consequently, motivation theories centered on these approaches are doomed to the same fate.

KOOCHER, GERALD P., JOHN C. NORCROSS, and SAM S. HILL, III, eds. *Psychologists' Desk Reference, Second Edition* (New York, NY: Oxford University Press, 2004). A key source for formulating a more formal description of some of the characters described in this book. It should be noted that the characters in this book are real, except for those that aren't.

LEFTON, ROBERT E., Ph.D., V. R. Buzzotta, Ph.D., Manuel Sherberg, and Dean L. Karraker. *Effective Motivation Through Performance Appraisal: Dimensional Appraisal Strategies* (New York, NY: John Wiley and Sons, Inc., 1977). An excellent example of the old way of thinking about motivation. "Written from the manager's point of view," this approach ignores the employee's perceptions about reality. It represents the state of one-sided motivation theory that was once prevalent.

MALLINGER, ALLAN E., M.D., and JEANNETTE DeWYZE. *Too Perfect: When Being in Control Gets Out of Control* (New York, NY: Clarkson N. Potter, 1991). Another look at human behavior vis à vis how the fear of uncertainty can foster obsessive behavior focused on attaining the impossible—perfectionism.

MILTON, JOYCE. *The Road to Malpsychia: Humanistic Psychology and Our Discontents* (San Francisco, CA: Encounter Books, 2002). Observations vis à vis the lack of long term progress with most behavioral modification theories.

MURPHY, TIM, Ph.D., and LORIANN HOFF OBERLIN. *Overcoming Passive–Aggression: How to Stop Hidden Anger from Spoiling Your Relationships, Career and Happiness*

(New York, NY: Marlowe & Company, 2005). A more detailed analysis of the type of behavior exhibited by Fred, the back office manager, and some of the more seemingly compliant, but actually negative, behavior of subordinates.

OFMAN, WILLIAM V. *Affirmation and Reality: Fundamentals of Humanistic Existential Therapy and Counseling* (New York, NY: Western Psychological Sciences, 1976). Reference provided to add balance to the notion that humanistic existentialism is not useful in understanding the difference between expected and real behavior. The author attempts to prove humanistic psychology useful in understanding and modifying human behavior.

OLDHAM, JOHN M., M.D., and LOIS B. MORRIS. *Personality Self-Portrait: Why You Think, Work, Love, and Act the Way You Do* (New York, NY: Bantam Books, 1990). A valuable resource for understanding the complexity of personalities. This book is a welcome departure from the superficiality of much of modern pop psychology. Based on the American Psychiatric Association diagnostic system, the text offers a self-test that when used properly can provide insight into how individuals feel and react in their various roles.

PAUL, ANNIE MURPHY. *The Cult of Personality: How Personality Tests Are Leading Us to Miseducate Our Children, Mismanage Our Companies, and Misunderstand Ourselves* (New York, NY: Free Press, 2004). An opposing view of the usefulness of personality testing. The author makes a good case for her contention that personality tests are leading us to a new level of minimally acceptable behavior and dysfunctional performance

RESTAK, RICHARD. *Poe's Heart and the Mountain Climber: Exploring the Effect of Anxiety on Our Brains and Our*

Culture (New York, NY: Harmony Books, 2004). An excellent approach to conceptualizing the concept as it relates to challenges to self-esteem and pressure to perform beyond our perceived capabilities.

SMITH, BARRY D., and HAROLD J. VETTER. *Theoretical Approaches to Personality* (Englewood Cliffs, NJ: Prentice-Hall, 1981). A complete guide to the understanding of psychodynamic, behavioral, cognitive, humanistic, factor, typological and field theories. An excellent reference book for those interested in exploring the elements of the thinking behind most motivation approaches.

SMITH, HOWARD ROSS. The concept behind Dr Spencer's way of thinking can be attributed first to a series of conversations with Howard Ross Smith, Chair of the Department of Management, University of Georgia. Also read Smith's *The Capitalistic Imperative: The New Biology and the Old Bureaucracy* (Hicksville, NY: Exposition-University Press, 1975). Dr Smith provides a captivating approach to understanding work behavior and motivation.

STORR, ANTHONY. *Solitude: A Return to the Self* (New York, NY: Free Press, 1988). An excellent source for anyone interested in the other side of conventional wisdom. Storr contends that isolation from society can be beneficial to the individual during periods of mourning and stress.

SVITIL, KATHY A. *Psychology Today: Calming the Anger Storm* (New York, NY: Alpha, 2006). A clear view of the complex emotion of anger. Either a positive approach to expressing frustration such as the dysfunctional loss of control as exhibited by Waldo Cluster, or the retro respective problem solving that comes with intelligence the elements of anger are addressed in an effective and efficient manner.

WEISS, ROBERT S. *Staying the Course: The Emotional and Social Lives of Men Who Do Well at Work* (New York, NY: Free Press, 1990). A review of the idea that successful people either lead unhappy lives of quiet desperation or that they are actually exploiters and part of an establishment of repression. The concept that the payoffs for successful people are as varied as those of anyone else provides a basis for understanding some elements of RCL.

WILMERDING, JOHN *Andrew Wyeth: The Helga Pictures* (New York, NY: Harry N Abrams, Inc., 1987)